THE
JOURNAL
OF NOT
KNOWING

A Workbook

THE
JOURNAL
OF NOT
KNOWING

A Workbook

CHARTING YOUR OWN COURSE

JULIE BENEZET

Author of *The Journey of Not Knowing:*
How 21st-Century Leaders Can Chart a Course Where There Is None

THE JOURNAL OF NOT KNOWING
CHARTING YOUR OWN COURSE
Julie Benezet

Published by Morton Hill Press
PO Box 614
Ashland, OR 97520
www.juliebenezet.com

ISBN 978-0-9978139-2-0

Library of Congress Control Number: 2018953384

Images from iStock, Getty Images, and Unsplash.

Content editor: Gail M. Kearns, www.topressandbeyond.com
Copyeditor: Joni Wilson
Book and cover design: *the*BookDesigners

*To the many generations of family members
who taught me the value of learning and
what a difference it can make.*

CONTENTS

INTRODUCTION TO

The Journal of Not Knowing

The twenty-first century changed the rules. While life has always had its challenges when new situations showed up, until now we thought we could handle them. After all, life was local. We knew the people, circumstances, and places that mattered to us. Familiarity gave us comfort that we had things under control, or so it seemed.

That comfort ended with the rise of the internet. With its global reach and instant transmission of massive amounts of information, we now inhabit a fast, hyperconnected world. Constant change is the norm. Whether we like it or not, people, circumstances, and places we don't know can have a direct impact on our lives. Much feels unpredictable, out of our control, and uncomfortable.

At least, that is one way of looking at it.

Another way is to see the shifting horizon not as an obstacle, but as a source of inspiration. Instead of running away from uncertainty, we can treat the unknown as a source of adventure, one that is rich with opportunities to make a difference to our teams, customers, and communities. Best of all, exploring new possibilities can bring meaning to our lives as we improve the lives of others.

Embarking on The Journey of Not Knowing®

Pursuing possibilities sets you on an uncharted path toward finding new solutions to sticky problems. The path can be uncomfortable. To uncover what people really want, you have to ask questions no one wants to answer, poke your nose into other people's business, and stare at things by the cold light of dawn, without the gloss of popular, preconceived notions.

Once your detective work leads you to a new idea, then you have to endure the uncomfortable process of testing it, without knowing whether the idea will succeed or fail. Not only do you have to satisfy yourself that the idea will work, you also have to convince others to join your experiment. Rather than responding enthusiastically, they might well resist your idea because of their own discomfort. **New ideas call for change, and change, even good change, is hard.**

The greatest resistance, however, might come from you. Change has its allure for the positive difference it can bring, but the road to the new can be bumpy, uncertain, and scary. You might end up in a ditch, get lost, or arrive at a different and wonderful place. It can go in any direction.

To smooth the bumps, you can slip into defensive behaviors, such as micromanagement, perfectionism, or disengagement. They bring short-term relief, but turning away rather than toward discomfort will take you off the course to achieving greater things.

Navigating the discomfort of the unknown in pursuit of new ideas is the central message of the book, *The Journey of Not Knowing: How 21st-Century Leaders Can Chart a Course Where There Is None*, a companion to this workbook. Leading and living in the twenty-first century requires *adopting a mindset that is comfortable with the discomfort of not knowing*.

In other words, initiating change means opening yourself to the emotional challenge of getting there—self-doubt, nervousness, edginess, fear. Such reactions are normal, yet you can expend a lot of energy fighting them. Moving to a better place involves learning that discomfort is a critical and exciting part of growth, for you and the organizations you lead.

What Is *The Journal of Not Knowing?*

The Journal of Not Knowing grew out of requests from readers of the *Journey* book who wanted to apply the lessons of the Arrow, Inc., story and the Journey of Not Knowing model to their own lives as leaders and individuals. The Arrow story describes a day in the life of an eight-member leadership team. To win a critical new piece of business, they have to explain to the board of Porter, Inc., the potential new client, why another client fired them. None of them knows why and, until Porter asked, none of them bothered to find out. The request sets them on a journey that requires each of them to overcome their defended behaviors and open the door to new information and growth.

This journal is intended to give you a place to explore your dreams, your relationship with the discomfort of the unknown, and your goals for the future. It combines questions, exercises, and other tools to spark ideas about where you would like to go, what past and present experiences influence your actions, and how to step out of your own way. It also will provide tools to chart a course through the new.

The workbook is designed for individuals and for teams. In other words, you can choose to work on it alone or in a group. If you prefer to work alone, I recommend discussing at least some of the questions with trusted friends, family members, or colleagues. It enriches self-discovery. It also can ease the tension of obsessive thinking that could make you feel unsure or frozen in place. There is nothing like hearing someone say, "No, you're not crazy. I've felt that way before," or, "Wow, given your situation, that idea sounds awesome!"

The Power of the Pen

In these digital days, writing with a pen might feel like an unnatural act. While it might seem strange to break away from a keyboard, multiple studies have shown that the kinesthetic action of handwriting can facilitate better concentration, increase commitment, and promote a higher level of recall when compared to keyboard entry. It also will enable you to scribble notes in the margins, circle concepts, and create images to chart your course along the twisting road to something more exciting.

DARE TO BE SELFISH

If you have read this far, you have already taken a significant step toward investing in yourself. Finding the time to work on personal growth in the twenty-first century requires a major commitment.

Dare to be selfish and devote time to yourself. The clarity you discover from working on your dreams and a route toward realizing them will release energy for you and those around you. After all, you are worth it.

THE POWER OF ACTION

Once you have recorded your thoughts in the journal, put them into action. Adopting new behaviors that accompany new ideas can feel awkward. Yet without traveling in the discomfort zone of the new, growth will not happen. The expression "growing pains" takes on special meaning when it comes to change. It is a visceral process with a power that cannot be denied. That is the adventure of living fully, sharing with others, and giving to yourself.

Enjoy the journey!

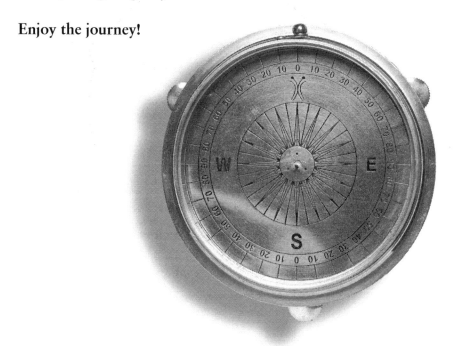

How to Use This Journal

This journal offers you a guide through *The Journey of Not Knowing* principles and an opportunity to apply them to your own life. It begins with your relationship with the unknown and the discomfort that comes with the new where the future is unknown. The journal then works through the core journey principles.

While the organization of the journal has a linear quality, brains work differently, having unique needs and learning styles. Feel free to skip around to wherever you want to go to do your best work.

THE TOOLKIT

1. **Questions:** You can write as little or as much as you want to focus your thoughts, ignite your imagination, and answer the questions.

2. **Exercises:** These are starting points. You are encouraged to go beyond them and dive deeper in this journal or in a separate notebook.

3. **Free Write:** The word "free" means just that. Do not edit, cut, or censor yourself. This journal is for your use only, unless you choose to share it. Allowing the thoughts to flow in whatever way or order they appear will bring you closer to your most honest feelings.

4. Checklists: These are starting points to inquiry. If they spur further insights, write them in the spaces provided or annotate in the margins. There is no extra credit for neatness. It is discouraged, unless it inspires you to think better.

5. Study Aids: Examples are given to catalyze your thinking if your find yourself stuck for an answer when working on an exercise.

6. Moments of Self-Reflection: These related insights could apply to any resistance you might have to the issues raised.

7. Lessons from the Front: These are stories that illustrate lessons about people who have embarked on their own journeys of not knowing.

8. Journey Snippets: To illustrate the material, included are a few examples from the Arrow, Inc., story in the *Journey* book.

9. Journey Mileposts: These summarize and reinforce the major themes of *The Journey of Not Knowing* for you to use in this journal and afterward.

CHAPTER I

The Journey of Not Knowing Model
The Core Four

Making a difference means taking chances. It sends you into unfamiliar places with unknown outcomes. The search for a new idea resembles entering a dark labyrinth with many unlit corridors. They twist, turn, and offer no directional signs to the exit. Finding your way through them can be scary, tempting you turn on your heels and escape out the entrance rather than dealing with the uncomfortable business of hunting for something better.

To test and build support for new ideas, you have to enter the discomfort zone of not knowing. The essential navigational tools you need to chart your course through the unknown are the Core Four, as set forth on the next page. They are described in greater detail later in this workbook and in Part 4 of the *Journey* book.

THE CORE FOUR

1. Bigger Bets: Pursue dreams to make life better.

A bigger bet is an idea for making a difference and lifting the game to satisfy a need not currently being met. The need can arise from your organization, affecting its team, customers, or community. It also can be personal, coming from something in your life you would like to change for the better.

2. The Risks of the Unknown: Get comfortable with the discomfort of risk.

New ideas move you into unfamiliar terrain where the outcome is unknown. All you know at the outset is that something will change as a result of you trying. Forging a new, unpredictable path carries with it the discomfort of risk.

3. Hooks: Watch out for self-sabotaging behaviors that will stand in the way of achieving your bigger bets.

When traveling on the uncomfortable new path toward your bigger bet, calming yourself with defensive behaviors is normal. They provide short-term relief. Defensive behaviors become "hooks" when they prevent you from pursuing your bigger bets.

4. Drivers: Find drivers to give you fuel for navigating the discomfort of the unknown.

A strong, personal motivator will provide you with a purpose to guide you through the discomfort of instigating change.

THE JOURNEY ROADMAP

The journey of not knowing roadmap covered by this journal starts with an exploration of the unknown that lies beneath the Core Four principles. It then delves into each of those principles. For each element, there is a set of key questions to create a frame for your journey into the new and unknown.

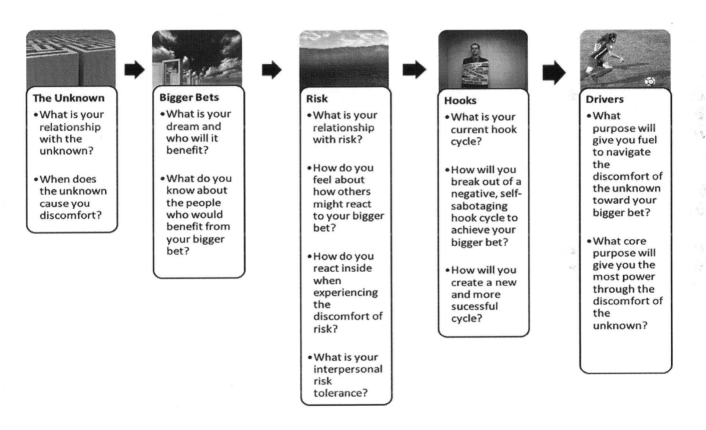

The Unknown

- What is your relationship with the unknown?

- When does the unknown cause you discomfort?

Bigger Bets

- What is your dream and who will it benefit?

- What do you know about the people who would benefit from your bigger bet?

Risk

- What is your relationship with risk?

- How do you feel about how others might react to your bigger bet?

- How do you react inside when experiencing the discomfort of risk?

- What is your interpersonal risk tolerance?

Hooks

- What is your current hook cycle?

- How will you break out of a negative, self-sabotaging hook cycle to achieve your bigger bet?

- How will you create a new and more sucessful cycle?

Drivers

- What purpose will give you fuel to navigate the discomfort of the unknown toward your bigger bet?

- What core purpose will give you the most power through the discomfort of the unknown?

The Unknown
What to Expect in Chapter 2

Before charting a course to pursue your dreams, it is important first to understand how the unknown shows up in your life, your reaction to it, and how you typically deal with the discomfort it causes.

Chapter 2 provides a two-part, deep dive into the discomfort of the unknown. The first part, "What is your relationship with the unknown?" guides you through exercises to gain insight on how you approach learning what is taking place around you (the "external unknown") and inside of you (the "internal unknown").

The second part, "When does the unknown cause you discomfort?" is where you will have an opportunity to identify and understand how discomfort might be preventing you from chasing after new ideas.

The Core Four Principles
What to Expect in Chapters 3 through 6

The Core Four strategies to confront the discomfort of the unknown when pursuing your dreams appear in Chapters 3 through Chapter 6. Under each principle are key questions that provide organizing guidelines with many questions, exercises, and tools within each to deepen your inquiry.

Strategic planning has a concept of putting stones into a bucket. First, you place your large stones at the bottom. These stones symbolize your most important goals. Around the large stones you fit many small stones, which, while important, represent secondary goals that support the large ones. Success comes from focusing first on the large stones. Then you know where the smaller ones fit.

The key questions under each Core Four principle aim to put into place the large stones. The small stones encourage further digging to add to what you learn about the big stones.

OVER THERE
NOWHERE
FAR AWAY
SOMEWHER
NO IDEA
NOT SURE
UNCERTAIN
DON'T KNOW
??
DISTANT

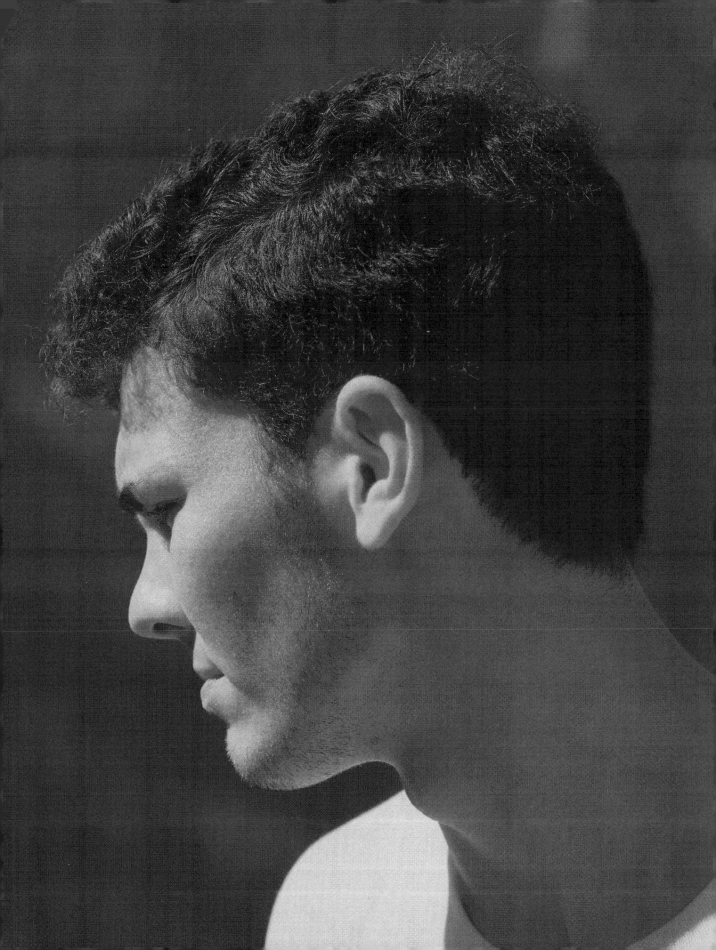

The Unknown
Laying the Foundation for Your Journey of Not Knowing

THE KEY QUESTIONS

> 1. WHAT IS YOUR RELATIONSHIP WITH THE UNKNOWN?

> 2. WHEN DOES THE UNKNOWN CAUSE YOU DISCOMFORT?

▶ 1. What is your relationship with the unknown?

Confronting the Labyrinth

———— EXERCISE ————

Imagine yourself standing in front of the entrance to a large labyrinth. The walls are tall. The opening to its interior is narrow, dark, and seems to lead nowhere. All you can see through the opening is a straight, unlit corridor. You can't see where it goes, much less where it exits, and you have no roadmap. Describe how you feel.

_____

_____

_____

_____

Some people respond to the image of the labyrinth entrance with the suggestion of grabbing a ladder to climb up and scan the distant horizon. Would that be of interest to you?

__Yes   __No   __Not really

Looking into the first long, dark corridor of the labyrinth, what are you inclined to do, or not do?

_____

_____

_____

_____

For many, not knowing where the exit lies is uncomfortable. They don't want to jump into something until they know where it ends up.

- Would you feel differently about the labyrinth if you could see the exit?

- Why or why not?

_____

_____

_____

_____

How willing are you to enter the labyrinth (with no ladder)? Below is a scale of 1 to 7. Circle the number that best describes you.

1. No way!	2. I'll think about it.	3. I'll be back later.	4. I'll try a few turns.	5. I'll go, but not alone.	6. Deep breath, here I go!	7. Just watch me!

What would move your number either up or down?

_____

_____

_____

_____

STUDY AID
Things Influencing Your Approach to the Labyrinth

- If you knew for sure where you would end up, would you circle #7?

- If someone told you that you had only a little time to find the exit, would you be less willing to try, circling #1, 2, or 3?

- If your manager or close friend said he or she would support you while you picked your way through the corridors, would that raise your number?

Think about your current organizational or personal life. Before you launch into something that is unfamiliar territory, how much do you need to know about it beforehand? Mark the statement that best describes you.

___Not much. I'll figure it out as I go.

___Enough to know there is a reasonable likelihood of success.

___Everything there is to know, and then some!

FREE WRITE

Describe your relationship with the unknown. Include any examples from your past that inform your present feelings. Go as far back as you want to go.

_____

_____

_____

_____

_____

_____

_____

_____

_____

_____

_____

_____

_____

_____

_____

_____

ENTERING THE LABYRINTH: *INVESTIGATING THE UNKNOWN*

Entering the unknown in pursuit of something new is a journey of discovery. Your mission is to explore facts and feelings you either did not know or understand, then use them to create a better future. The journey involves learning about external and internal unknowns. (For more on this topic, see Part 2 of the *Journey* book.)

The **external unknown** is what you don't know about the environment in which you work (or live if you are focusing on your personal life). It includes everything from the global economy to your group culture. To decide what direction to take, you have to peer around corners to learn what actually is happening around you, not just what you believe is taking place.

The **internal unknown** is what you don't know about yourself. To understand what is occurring in the world outside begins with you knowing what is going on inside of you. *Self-awareness is power.*

The journey into the internal unknown takes an inward look at how your life stories, values, and dreams for the future influence your behavior with new situations and people. It's important to examine different aspects of yourself, including old selves that in times of stress tug painfully at you like phantom limbs.

THE EXTERNAL UNKNOWN

—— EXERCISE ——

Choose a situation from your current life that bothers you. You might not know why it does. What you do know is that right now you are doing nothing about it.

> ### STUDY AID
> #### *Bothersome Situations*
>
> Below are some examples of questions that might be bothering you or that you might be avoiding. Do any sound familiar?
>
> • Why are your favorite customers not returning your calls?
>
> • Why at a team meeting do people just sit there, even when you ask direct questions?
>
> • Why did a long-term customer send her most recent project to a competitor?
>
> • Why was your engineering group not consulted before the sales organization changed the product description and left you to figure out how to build the product they described to customers, whether or not that is doable?
>
> • Why haven't you heard anything from a close friend and your attempts to contact her over several weeks have failed?
>
> • Why do your brother and sister just roll their eyes when you talk about leaving your job and returning to graduate school?

Briefly describe the situation and why you believe you have chosen to ignore it.

_____

_____

_____

What more would you like to know about the situation?

_____

_____

_____

_____

What has prevented you from asking those in a position to know about the situation? Remember to consider your own feelings and the possible reactions of others.

_____

_____

_____

_____

Do you want to do anything about it?

____Yes ____No ____No way!

If you answered "No" or "No way!" what would change your answer to "Yes"? For example, if you believed others had the same issue and would get behind you asking about it, would that make a difference? Or, if you saw others being rewarded for asking difficult questions, would that swing you to "Yes"?

_____

_____

_____

_____

DECODING THE UNKNOWN

——— EXERCISE ———

Look at the photo above. What do you see?

_____

_____

_____

_____

Most people see two adults, one or both of whom is a white male, one is wearing a dark sweater and the other wears a white sweater. The person in the black sweater has his hand up and appears to be talking.

Beyond those images, we have to start guessing. Is the person in the dark sweater angry, intense, in deep concentration? We can't tell by looking at the photo. Is the person in the white sweater listening, frowning, checked out? Do they know each other? Do they like each other? What led to this interaction?

The list goes on. The point is that in any situation, there are things we know, things we don't know but can find out, and things we cannot know, either because no one knows the answer or the person with the answers is not willing to reveal them. There are also things that cannot be known by anyone, such as the exact date a major hurricane will hit next year.

The pursuit of the new to make things better will land you in a direct line of travel toward many things you do not know. You start with some obvious perceptions such as those listed in the **Study Aids—Bothersome Situations** box. You can witness behaviors, read information, and listen to the words people say, *but you don't know what lies beneath.*

To come up with an idea to make things better, you begin by assessing what you know, then search for answers about the many things you don't know. It can be a long, humbling list. Without knowing the facts, you won't be able to generate an idea that will get people's attention, much less give them what they (or you) want.

Cirque du Soleil reinvented the circus after exploring why the demand for circus entertainment had significantly declined. When the Cirque du Soleil founders peered under the covers of what had been long-held assumptions about circus customers, they learned several new things.

- First, the public had become uncomfortable with the use of animals in circus acts.

- Second, having three rings rather than one caused angst among customers, as they had to switch their attention back and forth among three centers of activity.

- Third, replacing random acts (by clowns, acrobats, and animals) with a consistent storyline, presented in a more artistic setting, appealed to an audience that was choosing between the circus and the live entertainment industry of theatre.

The reward for the Cirque du Soleil founders learning what they did not know about the target audience was the creation of a visibly rich, clever theatrical offering that generated in 2017 annual revenues of over $845 million.

Then there are the things you can never know. That is because they involve behavior of which a person has no awareness, much less insight, or knows about it but refuses to share with you. It can be maddening, but it is the reality of human behavior. There are also those matters for which answers cannot yet be found, such as the definitive cure for all cancers.

When you embark into the unknown in search of answers to what people need, your job is to confirm what you know and to learn what you don't know but can find out. You learn by asking questions, researching data, and observing with no agenda other than to uncover the reality of a situation. For those things you can never know, your challenge is to become peaceful with that reality, but also to keep your eyes and ears open should something change.

--- EXERCISE ---

For the bothersome situation you identified previously, or, if you like, choose another, answer the following questions.

What do you know about it?

_____

_____

_____

What don't you know and need to find out?

These could be questions such as "What is his relationship with the new executive? What is her level of expertise with a newly released company product? Did the person who seems to be ignoring you actually receive your messages?"

_____

_____

_____

_____

What might you never know?

For example, someone might never reveal to you their painful and repressed personal history with bullies that affects how they behave when confronted with a bullying authority figure.

_____

_____

_____

_____

LESSONS FROM THE FRONT
Taking the Plunge

The owner of a real estate services company dived into the unknown by transforming a small mom-and-pop brokerage firm into a medium-sized company. The change did not happen overnight. The owner spent several years before that with a small staff providing brokerage and third-party property management services to a diversity of public and private clients.

She worked long hours juggling two lines of business, managing employees, and dreaming of something bigger. She wanted to build a company that provided corporate real estate services to companies that lacked real estate expertise.

To realize that dream, she knew she would have to go after larger contracts, expand her staff, and increase her financial exposure. All of those consequences scared her. She spent many sleepless nights worrying about not knowing what would happen if she took on those risks. At the same time, the dream of creating something bigger grew larger.

At a weekend retreat with trusted friends from the real estate industry, she shared her dream. Emboldened by the enthusiastic support she received, she couldn't stand any more internal churning. It was time to take the plunge.

Later on, she reported back to her friends. "So, I decided that even though I had no idea how things would turn out, how was I going to find out if I didn't just jump in and try? Finally, one day I did it and, wow, so many good things started to happen!"

What happened was that when she expanded her staff, services, and geographical reach, her business grew substantially. It was scary, fun, and satisfying. Three years later, a global company acquired her business.

THE INTERNAL UNKNOWN

The same principles for the external unknown of what you know, what you don't know but can find out, and what you will never know apply to the internal unknown.

Before interacting with someone, becoming clear about your own motives, actions, and reactions will improve the quality of the conversation, the information you glean from it, and produce better results. Getting clear is no small order. Humans are complicated. That makes them interesting, frustrating, and full of potential.

What internal influences do we bring to our interactions with other people?

In any interaction, you bring three key attributes that filter what you are able to learn. If you don't understand what is clogging the filter, you will get less reliable information.

1. Your needs: What do you care about?

- to feel powerful
- friendship
- to be acknowledged
- to be viewed as smart
- promotion
- to control a situation that feels uncontrollable
- technical information to write a report

These are just a few examples.

2. Your perceptions: What affects how you take in information?

- Your perceptions, that is, what your five senses detect, and any factors that might inhibit sensing (for example, nearsightedness, noisiness of the room, physical distance from key players, etc.).

  - Our senses pick up many dimensions of information, far more than we realize in the moment. You might wonder after a conversation why you found yourself walking away from a person feeling strange. Then you recall his loud voice and how you instinctively pulled away, remembering how loud male voices remind you of your domineering father.

- Your history with the person in question and its impact on how you take in sensory information when with them.

    - For example, if you had an argument with the person earlier, you might perceive their facial expression as hostile, when in reality, they might have already forgotten the run-in. It is also possible that the hostility you feel might be your own projection.

3. Your emotional and physical state: What are you thinking and feeling?

- What is your mental state? Are you stressed, relaxed, apprehensive, excited?

- What is your physical state? Are you tired, alert, hungry, headachy?

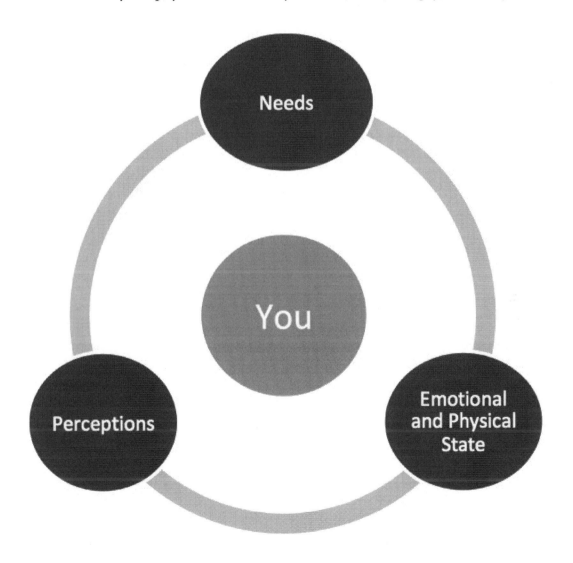

—————————— EXERCISE ——————————

Think about a person or a situation that bothers you.

Describe briefly that person or a situation in which a person is involved.

_____

_____

_____

_____

What might influence how you understand what the person involved is doing or thinking?

Your needs

_____

_____

_____

_____

Your perceptions

_____

_____

_____

_____

Your emotional and physical state

_____

_____

_____

_____

STUDY AID
Unclogging the Filters

Here are some examples of strategies to help you think about how to improve what you learn and accomplish with another person.

- Know specifically what you need from the person. Make lists, be focused, and deliberate. If free writing helps you to organize your thinking, start with it.

- If you are not feeling physically well, if possible, postpone talking with the person until you feel better.

- If you had a bad experience with someone whose backing you now need, analyze what happened between you and that person. What did they do to violate your trust, how might you have contributed to the issue, and how willing are you to let bygones be bygones in the name of advancing your cause? Consider brainstorming your answers with a trusted advisor.

- Be aware that whomever you need to support your goals has their own needs, perceptions, and physical and emotional state that will influence how they respond to you. Before approaching them, do your homework to learn about their needs, history with the issue you want to discuss, and anything else that will enable you to see, hear, and understand them as clearly as possible.

Based on what you wrote about your needs, perceptions, and emotional and physical state, and using the Study Aid strategies, what can you do to clear up confusing signals and take a more informed approach to dealing with the person?

1. _____

2. _____

3. _____

4. _____

5._____

JOURNEY MILEPOST
The Unknown

New ideas come without a roadmap. To try them out, you have to move through unfamiliar corridors, not knowing who or what you will meet along the way. The journey starts with recognizing how you approach or avoid new people and situations, and how open you are to building something better, knowing that the new involves uncertainty.

The more willing you are to search for new information to understand what is happening around you and inside of you, the better positioned you will be to create new ideas and make them happen.

A key to navigating the unknown is to learn from each encounter and course correct as needed.

▶ 2. WHEN DOES THE UNKNOWN CAUSE YOU DISCOMFORT?

ENTERING THE DISCOMFORT ZONE

When you know what is going on, whether you like it or not, at least you can find a solution. Fixing it might be a hassle, but at least you know what has to be changed, and what you personally can do about it.

For example, you hear there is a new vacation policy, but missed its announcement. You had already planned a vacation without knowing about the new policy and want to find out if your trip falls within the new rules. Knowing that a new policy exists, you can contact whichever department manages vacation policies to ascertain whether you have a problem and how to resolve it.

What causes you discomfort is when you don't know something that might be happening, which could have an impact on you.

—————————— EXERCISE ——————————

1. Think of something that might be going on in your business or personal life right now that you are uncomfortable not knowing.

STUDY AID
Sources of Discomfort

- Are they going to fund your project?
- Will they finally promote you if you win this deal?
- Did they like your presentation?
- Why have your brother and sister-in-law not gotten back to you on whether they will invest in your new business idea?
- Do your peers or family members understand how much energy you expend advocating on their behalf to make sure they are appreciated by others?

_____

_____

_____

_____

2. Why does not knowing what might be happening make you feel uncomfortable?

_____

_____

_____

_____

DEBRIEF AND NEXT STEPS

Consider asking a trusted friend or colleague to discuss with you what you are uncomfortable not knowing. Then answer these questions after your conversation.

1. How did it feel to talk about something you had not previously discussed with anyone?

Check all that apply.

    ___Sense of relief

    ___Awkward

    ___Unsafe

    ___Weird

___Energizing

___Other _____

_____

_____

2. Did it help you in any way to talk about it with another person? Why or why not?

_____

_____

_____

LESSONS FROM THE FRONT
The Impact of Sharing

In the *Journey* programs, we found that when even private people share concerns with others, it has the impact of lightening the emotional load of the stress about not knowing something, regardless of whether they learned more about the situation itself. For many, downloading the swirling in their heads had the impact of arresting obsessive stewing. Then they were able to switch gears to uncover new insights and solutions.

THE DISCOMFORT OF CONSEQUENCES

*"Comfort sits in the middle of what is known,
and people are already doing that."*
—*The Journey of Not Knowing*

Undertaking the detective work to explore new surroundings can come from a place of intellectual curiosity where the sleuthing alone will propel you. However, if you find yourself avoiding unfamiliar halls, it might be that you suspect entering them has consequences.

It begs the question, why is that? Aside from the anxiety of anticipating unforeseen events, running through your mind might be an imaginary list of bad things that could occur as a result of launching a new direction. Try the following exercise on what fears might lie beneath any reluctance you sense about promoting a new idea.

———————————— EXERCISE ————————————

You decide to take the bold move of proposing a change in direction to your organization. You are excited about what you want to do, but, at the same time, something holds you back. Inside your head runs a noisy conversation of fear, self-doubt, and second-guessing.

Do any of the statements in the checklist sound like the conversation inside your head? For each item, check "Yes," "No," or "Maybe." This is not an intelligence test, but rather an opportunity to build self-awareness. Don't overthink this. Feel free to add your own sources of reluctance.

CHECKLIST
The Consequences of New Ideas That Cause Me Discomfort

When I think about trying my new idea, I worry that . . .	Yes	No	Maybe
Others will laugh at me for suggesting the idea.			
It might not work and hurt my credibility.			
Nobody suggested it before, because everyone else already thought of it and thinks it's really stupid.			
It could cost me my job.			
People will stop seeing me as successful.			
My peers might see me as too ambitious.			
Someone might try to steal my idea, claiming it as theirs.			
If the idea fails, I could lose the trust others have in me.			
If the idea works, I might end up getting promoted over my best friend.			
I don't know how to defend my idea.			
If the idea is accepted, then I will be stuck with the responsibility for its execution *and* success.			

List other possibilities that cause you discomfort.

_____

_____

_____

Do you have any additional concerns about potential consequences?

_____

_____

_____

Remember a time when you proposed a new idea to a group and it turned out to be successful. What did you experience emotionally between the moment the idea hit you and when you knew it was a success? Include such things as your worries, reactions of others, your reaction to their reactions, events that made you want to stop, and what kept you moving forward.

_____

_____

_____

_____

_____

How realistic were your fears? Knowing then what you know now, would you have gone ahead with it? Why or why not? What did you learn?

_____

_____

_____

_____

MOMENT OF SELF-REFLECTION

When you see someone else trying out a new idea, what do you think?

____How stupid!

____Wow, that took guts.

____Really?

____What is she trying to prove?

FREE WRITE

Why are you being so critical? Does that person deserve your criticism, or could you be projecting your own discomfort with the risk of change?

_____

_____

_____

_____

_____

_____

_____

_____

_____

JOURNEY MILEPOST
The Value of the Discomfort Zone

Entering the discomfort zone when trying something new begins with acknowledging how you respond to unknown people and situations. You might balk, feel nervous, or act tentatively. There is nothing wrong with those reactions. There is everything right with them. It means you are paying attention to life as it really is, hard as that might be, rather than how you would like it to be.

Seeing life as realistically as you can also means you won't know ahead of time how things will unfold when you try your new idea. If you did know ahead of time, the idea is not new and will take you down the road of "same old, same old." As the expression says, "The definition of insanity is doing the same thing over and over and expecting different results." Put differently, if the old idea had solved the problem, the problem would have gone away.

LAUNCHING THE JOURNEY OF NOT KNOWING
The Core Four Principles

In Chapter 2, you investigated your relationship with the unknown and any discomfort it might cause you. The next four chapters explore navigating the discomfort of the unknown through the lens of a bigger bet you would like to pursue, applying the Core Four principles.

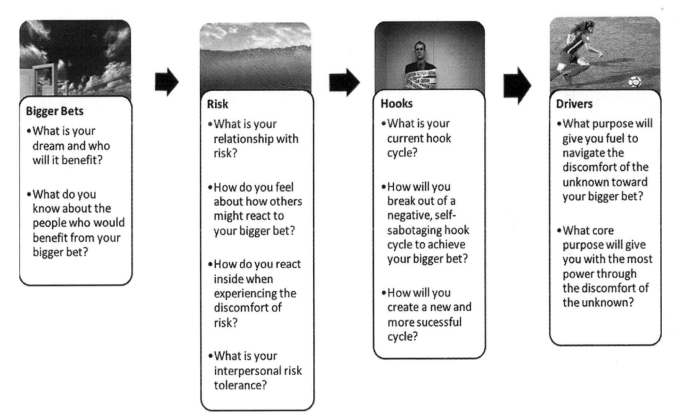

Bigger Bets

- What is your dream and who will it benefit?

- What do you know about the people who would benefit from your bigger bet?

Risk

- What is your relationship with risk?

- How do you feel about how others might react to your bigger bet?

- How do you react inside when experiencing the discomfort of risk?

- What is your interpersonal risk tolerance?

Hooks

- What is your current hook cycle?

- How will you break out of a negative, self-sabotaging hook cycle to achieve your bigger bet?

- How will you create a new and more sucessful cycle?

Drivers

- What purpose will give you fuel to navigate the discomfort of the unknown toward your bigger bet?

- What core purpose will give you with the most power through the discomfort of the unknown?

CHAPTER 3

Your Bigger Bets
Pursue Dreams to Make Life Better

THE KEY QUESTIONS

1. WHAT IS YOUR DREAM AND WHO WILL IT BENEFIT?

2. WHAT DO YOU KNOW ABOUT THE PEOPLE WHO WOULD BENEFIT FROM YOUR BIGGER BET?

Dare to Dream

Welcome to the world of entrepreneurship, the place where you pursue the new, despite feeling unsure, tested, and at the mercy of the judgment of others. Your ideas might succeed, fail, or lead you to a recalibrated plan that works. The journey of not knowing can be a scary road to travel, but its reward is generativity, purpose, and growth.

The next four chapters will focus on the Core Four, the navigational tools to guide you through the discomfort of not knowing in pursuit of the new. They start with your dreams.

▶ 1. What is your dream and who will it benefit?

A bigger bet is a new idea for making a difference and lifting the game to satisfy a need not currently being met. Your ideas don't have to change the course of history, but rather will make something better than it was before. (See Part 4 of the *Journey* book.)

Bigger bets cover a wide range of new ideas. They can touch any facet of your organizational or personal life. In business or other organizations, they cover a wide range, from a new engineering process that uses digital integration to speed up product delivery to a team culture where everyone has an equal vote on hiring policies.

Personal bigger bets can involve changing careers, leaving a steady job to form a political group to fight for a local cause, or launching a new health regime that requires a radical reworking of work and family responsibilities.

The common thread is a bigger bet strives to make things better.

The Target Group

Critical to creating a bigger bet is identifying your target group. In other words, whose lives are you trying to improve? In organizations, the group can be your employees, team, customers, shareholders, or community.

If you are working on a personal bigger bet, think about who might benefit as a result of your change. They could be family members, your spouse, partner, friends, or a formal or informal group with whom you are involved.

Once you choose your target group, your next step is to learn all you can about their needs to hone your idea and win their support. You also need to know your own needs, whether you are pursuing an organizational or personal bigger bet, because you are the one who has to make it work. Learning what you and others want means going to places that might be unknown to you, places where you have to meet new people, acquire new skills, or learn a different culture. That might feel awkward or uncomfortable, but that is what the journey of not knowing is about!

Here are some examples of bigger bets and the importance of making the time and effort to learn about target groups.

- If you are in real estate development, few people other than design professionals can visualize a building before it is built. Nevertheless, clients are constantly asked to give direction to the design team about how the building should look. A bigger bet that creates clearer, less conventional, 3D designs for clients to see more easily how the final building will look could arm both the design team and their clients to make smarter decisions.

- If you are in the nonprofit world, you might work on new models for crowdsourcing after studying donor behavior at a deeper level, asking target donors more personal questions about what motivates them to write checks (for example, "What makes you want to contribute money to a cause? What campaign messaging or methods turn you off?").

- If you want to publish the stories from a group of childhood friends who have helped one another weather many life transitions, you first will have to discover their personal boundaries on private information, willingness to revisit difficult memories, and their abilities to recall what they actually did to overcome hard times. Without answering these questions, you won't be able to collect their stories.

A bigger bet stretches you when you head toward a new idea that might not yet have a name. It might reflect an instinct you have or come out of a preliminary analysis. In whatever way it arrives, your willingness to jump in and learn about how you can create positive change could lead to something wonderful.

LESSONS FROM THE FRONT
A Tale from Early Amazon Days

The Issue: When I arrived at Amazon.com in 1998 as its first global real estate executive, I entered a hyperpaced, constantly changing work environment with few rules, systems, or operating histories. That was fun but tough when we needed to obtain approvals for our many multimillion dollar real estate leases. With no approval process, my reward for presenting a carefully negotiated lease to the daily officer in charge (usually our chief financial officer) was pushback. When she questioned the business case for a deal, rather than confirming their earlier approvals, the members of the leadership team ran for cover.

The Dilemma: As the lawyer in me still lived, I had retained every email and handwritten note showing they had indeed approved the deals. However, rather than litigating the issue with them, I decided on a different strategy. With the help of our vice president of tax, I organized an integrated real estate strategy group that would vet and approve every major lease.

My Bigger Bet: The group, affectionately called "Real Estate SWAT," became my bigger bet. Its purpose was to overcome the lack of information flow and alignment on our major real estate transactions, then obtain approvals from everyone. My target group was the leaders of key functional groups. What I knew was they had no time or expertise to think through their real estate requirements, but a high need for the real estate itself. Given the warp speed at which we worked, we had no room for late delivery of real estate to house our exploding growth.

Real Estate SWAT met for one hour a week with senior leaders from every major company function, including all the countries in which we had business operations. We banged through each company initiative that needed real estate facilities. We learned about their business goals (headcount growth, product throughput, cross border dependencies, etc.) and with that information, we could confirm their business requirements, ask follow-up questions, and collect approvals.

The Outcome: The SWAT bigger bet served as Amazon's first integrated strategic planning function. It proved to be highly popular, as it was the one place in the company where people could go to get a bigger picture of where Amazon was headed. SWAT served its purpose. We pushed through over 35 leases in 18 months. We disbanded the group when Amazon instituted a formal financial planning process.

— EXERCISE —

1. Think about a dream you have that you would like to pursue. Your bigger bet can address a challenge you have in your whole organization, a specific group (team, company, customer, etc.), or your personal life. It also might be something you have been avoiding because the risk involved in pulling it off is significant for you.

Describe a challenge you want to solve and the people or group who are affected by it.

_____

_____

_____

_____

STUDY AID
Sample Bigger Bets

- Inventing a new customer service model that has office hours when customers can talk directly with specialty technicians.

- Developing a process that pairs remote workers with champions in the main office to help them find the resources, people, and internal company news to keep them on top of things.

- Creating a collaborative culture that promotes and enforces candid feedback.

- Starting a how-to blog that advises people about dealing with bullies.

---

2. What dream or bigger bet would you like to pursue to solve that challenge?

_____

_____

_____

_____

▶ 2. WHAT DO YOU KNOW ABOUT THE PEOPLE WHO WOULD BENEFIT FROM YOUR BIGGER BET?

Creating a successful bigger bet requires that you educate yourself about the challenge underlying it. Too many times, what initially seems like a great new strategic idea fails because the people promoting it did not do their homework. Rather than spending the time to go out and ask a lot of questions about the underlying problem, they make assumptions, usually wrong ones. Their reward is a failed bigger bet.

Hard as it might be to take that time, and, even harder, demand people's attention to answer awkward questions they might not want to answer or admit they can't, your detective work will pay large dividends in developing a winning bigger bet.

In short, you have to venture into the unknown to surface information critical to your success.

──────────────── EXERCISE ────────────────

In the table, write the names of the people (or groups) who are affected by the challenge you've chosen and who would benefit by the well-designed bigger bet. **List the people experiencing the impact of the challenge, including those who have to buy into it because they are decision makers and those who have to implement it.**

Use your discretion as to where a group would suffice to describe an affected party and where there are individuals whose influence is strong enough to list separately from a group. For example, you might need to convince the marketing department to feature the diversity of your consulting team in the company promotional materials, but it is the director of marketing, not the group, who has to decide on the marketing content and she believes diversity is not an issue.

Who are they?	What do you know about their needs, as they relate to your challenge?	What don't you know about their needs, and have to learn?

3. After you go on your learning expedition to interview the people affected by your bigger bet, do you need to modify the bigger bet to fit the new information you gathered? If so, what is your updated bigger bet?

_____

_____

_____

_____

LESSONS FROM THE FRONT
Beware of the "Black Holes" in Change Initiatives

When initiating change, watch out for the "black hole" effect.

A senior executive at a product design firm launched a bigger bet that proposed to change the way project teams chose their members. Instead of team managers deciding who would and would not be on a team, the senior executive's bigger bet would give the power of team membership to the team members themselves. When told of the initiative, the team managers were a bit nervous but trusted the judgment of the senior executive and went along with the idea.

In teeing up the bigger bet, the senior executive spent all his time soliciting feedback and buy-in from his team managers, but did not involve the people on the project teams who would experience the direct impact of the change. The executive had assumed the managers had talked with them and they had bought into the change. Unfortunately, that was not the case. The managers had left the announcement of the change to the executive, sidestepping any potential controversy that might have erupted.

When an oversight such as this occurs, the people who were not included in the decision-making process might greet the bigger bet with resentment and react by sabotaging the idea with mediocre execution, passive resistance, or outright revolt. In other words, the cost of leaving them out of the process can be high.

In the case of the product design firm, the team members did not understand how the system would work and how much authority they actually would have. It took a lot of meetings and time to appease the crowd before they could launch the new team selection approach with the support of the team members themselves.

To maximize success of a bigger bet, the campaign to win backing for the change should include vetting it in advance with the people who will be most affected.

JOURNEY MILEPOST
The Quest for the New

Going after your dreams can be scary, hard, and exhilarating. We may not know why we even want to go there, but, for some reason, we have an itch that has to be scratched that might also feel good to others. To put in place a bigger bet, we begin by understanding what need it will satisfy and what we need to know about the people the idea will affect.

Think of life as a laboratory where new ideas get tested. In contrast to a science lab, however, bigger bets have to touch people in a way that not only makes sense to them, but they have to believe it is worth doing.

53

CHAPTER 4

The Risk of the Unknown
Getting Comfortable with the Discomfort of Risk

THE KEY QUESTIONS

▶ 1. WHAT IS YOUR RELATIONSHIP WITH RISK?

▶ 2. HOW DO YOU FEEL ABOUT HOW OTHERS MIGHT REACT TO YOUR BIGGER BET?

▶ 3. HOW DO YOU REACT INSIDE WHEN EXPERIENCING THE DISCOMFORT OF RISK?

▶ 4. WHAT IS YOUR INTERPERSONAL RISK TOLERANCE?

THE OPPORTUNITY OF RISK

New ideas move you into the unfamiliar places that promise no certain outcome. All you know is that something will change as a result of you trying. Trying something new brings with it the scariness of risk.

To many, the mere sound of the word risk is threatening. It conjures up images of being out of control, vulnerable, or unsafe. At the same time, it is an indispensable part of pursuing the new. When you don't know how the future will play out, it's hard to know how getting there will look, much less feel.

The pursuit of a bigger bet involves risk. Asking people questions about problems they haven't solved could stir up sensitivity. Because you don't know how they will respond, or if they will respond, it is important first to understand your relationship with taking risks, including the behavioral risks that come with uncomfortable conversations.

Learning how to manage the scariness of risk will build your self-confidence as you become accustomed to embracing it as an asset rather than a liability. Knowing how you react to new situations is important to tolerating uncertainty and seeing it as a normal part of the process. Armed with self-knowledge about how you face fearful situations will equip you to see the unexpected as an opportunity.

▶ 1. WHAT IS YOUR RELATIONSHIP WITH RISK?

Imagine yourself standing in the water at a beach on a calm day. All of a sudden, a wave rises up in front of you. You are not close enough to shore to step away from the impact of the wave. What three words describe how you experience it? Be honest with yourself.

1. _____

2. _____

3. _____

Did you—(Check all that apply)

___Freeze?

___Want to try running to shore?

___Look around for someone to rescue you?

___Wish to scream?

___Wait for the wave to pick you up and slam you on the beach (then drag you out to sea again)?

___Want to dive under that wave, not knowing whether on the other side would appear another wave, or the wide-open sea?

___Other? _____

Reading what you wrote, what strikes you about how you responded?

_____

_____

_____

For some, comparing your reaction to the unexpected to the sudden swell of an ocean wave might feel too abstract. Or, you are one of those people who thrive on physical danger but not so much the unforeseen human behavior in the work world. In the latter case, you have lots of company.

Office life offers endless examples of unexpected events and behaviors. For example, your manager blows into your office yelling at the top of his voice about a last-minute assignment, or a colleague calls you out in front of your whole team for missing a step in a new process you have been testing. Family dinner tables provide endless examples of surprising behavior. Whatever happens, these places are the playing field in which you have to operate to achieve your bigger bets.

▶ 2. HOW DO YOU FEEL ABOUT HOW OTHERS MIGHT REACT TO YOUR BIGGER BET?

You can't be sure ahead of time how people will react to your questions about your bigger bet. They might resent you suggesting there is a problem, dislike your suggestion because it means more work for them, or think your idea is stupid. They might also find your idea intriguing, feel pleased you took the initiative, or want to learn more. Anything can happen. Anticipating their possible reactions can help prepare you for gaining their support and addressing their concerns.

——————————— EXERCISE ———————————

Facing the unknown reactions of others to your bigger bet

1. Return to the bigger bet you chose in Chapter 3. Read through the list of individuals and groups affected by it. How do you think each of them will react to your bigger bet? How does their potential reaction land with you? Either short or long answers will do.

Who will be affected by your bigger bet?	How might they react to it?	How would you feel about that reaction?

2. When you reflect on the possible reactions, do you feel any differently about talking with them about your bigger bet?

___Yes

___No

___Probably

Will it change your course of action? If so, how?

_____

_____

_____

▶ 3. HOW DO YOU REACT INSIDE WHEN EXPERIENCING THE DISCOMFORT OF RISK?

When you are driving to create and test a bigger bet, you will find yourself in many situations you can't control, much less foresee the outcome. When you have been there before with a bigger bet and you experienced discomfort, what happened to you emotionally and physically?

It is important to notice and honor your discomfort. Ignoring it will not make it go away. Instead, use it as a signal that you are up to something new.

To understand how you cope with risk, it helps to recognize what goes on inside of your head, body, and heart. Armed with self-knowledge, you can more easily accept your reactions as real and honor them as a part of who you are.

FREE WRITE

When you anticipate interacting with others about your bigger bet, what sensations do you experience in your head, body, and heart?

Write your answers to the questions below.

HEAD: What conversations occur inside your head?

> ### STUDY AID
> #### *Conversations in Your Head*
>
> Below are some possibilities. If any of these apply, check or add them to your response.
>
> ___I hate even the thought of risk.
>
> ___I dread losing control of a situation, and I have no idea how this will go.
>
> ___I'm afraid to start a conversation in case others react badly.
>
> ___I don't have the energy to deal with the blowback.
>
> ___I don't know if I can face my team if this fails.
>
> ___If I succeed, will expectations go up for me?
>
> ___What could possibly make this worth it to me?

_____

_____

_____

_____

_____

_____

BODY: What is happening inside your body?

STUDY AID
Noticing Physical Reactions to Risk

When faced with a new situation, remember to take time to notice how you respond physically. Whether the novelty scares or elates you, your body will react in some way. The more familiar you are with how you respond, the easier it will be to accept its signals.

Start by pausing to check on what your body is doing. Try to focus specifically on what is happening. The list below this Study Aid will give you a guide to many common reactions. If it helps you, describe your physical state to a trusted colleague or friend for reassurance and to share experiences.

If any of these possible physical reactions apply, check or add them to your response.

Do you feel—

____Your heart pounding fast?

____Faster breathing?

____A knot in the stomach?

____Tight shoulders?

____A chilly calm?

____A rush?

____A need to bolt?

____Energized

____Other? _____

_____

Describe your experience. For example, when you anticipate proposing your bigger bet to others, do you find yourself overwhelmed by physical sensations that makes it hard to think? Or, do you become so shaky with excitement that you can't wait to make your pitch?

_____

_____

_____

_____

_____

_____

_____

HEART: What emotions hit you when you think about initiating your bigger bet?

> ### STUDY AID
> *Emotional Reactions*
>
> What you might be feeling.
>
> • I love the pursuit and the thrill of not knowing how it will end up.
>
> • I have a nervous, push-pull feeling. If it doesn't work, what then? But what if it does?
>
> • I feel confident.
>
> • I'm afraid of what might happen if it actually works and they want more than I have the energy to deliver.
>
> • I'm terrified to ask for help on where to start with this idea.
>
> • I feel reluctant about going forward with my bigger bet, because I'd have to work with some people I don't trust and whose values I don't share.
>
> • I'm eager to get started!

_____

_____

_____

_____

_____

_____

―――――――――――― EXERCISE ――――――――――――

How would you briefly summarize how you react inside to risk and how will you use your self-knowledge to your advantage?

_____

_____

_____

_____

STUDY AID
Managing Internal Reactions to Risk
The Pep Talk

You notice when entering a meeting where you will present your new initiative that your brain starts to spin with an internal monologue of self-doubt, your shoulders get tight, and you feel anxious about remembering all you have to say and still show enthusiasm. If you know this is how you are likely to react, remind yourself of it.

Then give yourself a pep talk: "A-yup, I am starting that old self-doubt thing, my shoulders are tight as cement, and I'm scared I won't be able to put subject and verb together. I guess I must be up to something good to feel this bad! Well, I made it through this the last time and I will again! How else can I make things happen around here?"

Write some thoughts on what you will do to notice and accept your internal reactions and allow them to remind you of what you are trying to achieve.

_____

_____

_____

_____

MOMENT OF SELF-REFLECTION
Avoidance Behaviors

FREE WRITE

When writing about what is going on in your head, body, and heart, are you tempted to distance yourself from your reactions, surfing the news, scanning social media, or grabbing a snack? Why is that? What concerns to you have?

_____

_____

_____

_____

_____

_____

BIGGER BETS AND RISK

Bigger bets do not have to change the rotation of the planet. They do need to make things better by coming up with a new direction, process, or behavior that will make a difference. While the potential for success brings excitement to the experiment, the risk of failure is real. You will know if you are on the right track to something new and better if you feel some level of nervousness. If you don't experience at least some edge of apprehension, you probably have not pushed far enough. For example, why ask only that people embrace a culture of mutual respect, when your real concern is the failure to give one another useful feedback?

Discomfort occurs in different ways, depending on the person and the complexity of what you sign up to change. It's important to respect your feelings but not let it stop you from moving ahead.

Trying out your bigger bet will be less stressful if you recognize that the discomfort you experience is not a sign that you are crazy, but rather that you have embarked on an important journey where such feelings are normal and important. They will heighten your awareness of how things are going, validate the process, and energize you.

LESSONS FROM THE FRONT
"Stay with Me!"

In an early scene of the movie *Gladiator*, Russell Crowe, playing a Roman general, leads his troops through a spooky forest. It's apparent they don't know where their enemies are hiding or how to get through the forest. Russell Crowe's character didn't know either, but he knew how to command his troops, "Stay with me! Stay with me!"

His confidence in knowing the importance of staying together and pushing through the forest demonstrated what he as a leader was there to do. You don't have to know how an unknown situation ends up. Your job is to know how to pursue the answer.

―――――――――――――――― EXERCISE ――――――――――――――――

Choose either the bigger bet you explored in this chapter or some other dream that involves risk.

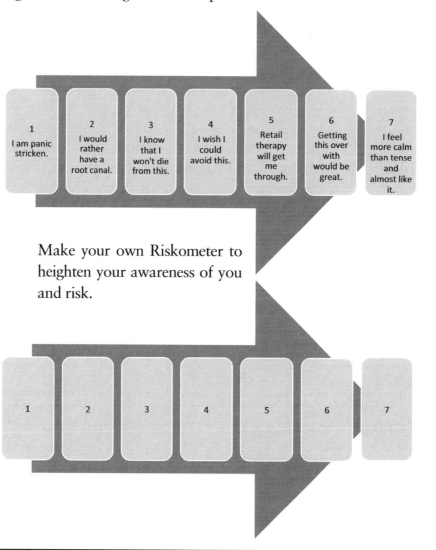

STUDY AID
Riskometer

While the examples in this continuum of risk-related anxiety might not speak to you, one way to manage your nervousness is to start by defining your own continuum. Circle what level of discomfort you are feeling. A rating of "1" is the highest level of perceived risk and "7" is the lowest.

1	2	3	4	5	6	7
I am panic stricken.	I would rather have a root canal.	I know that I won't die from this.	I wish I could avoid this.	Retail therapy will get me through.	Getting this over with would be great.	I feel more calm than tense and almost like it.

Make your own Riskometer to heighten your awareness of you and risk.

How would you describe your level and experience of anxiety about taking risks to advance a bigger bet?

_____

_____

_____

_____

▶ 4. WHAT IS YOUR INTERPERSONAL RISK TOLERANCE?

Taking on the quest for new ideas involves other people—informing, cajoling, and ultimately winning their buy-in. The process of getting there can be awkward. It requires holding new conversations, challenging old assumptions, and digging up insights you did not know were there.

Critical to achieving your bigger bet is understanding that you don't know at the outset is how others will behave. The questions and actions you ask of others during your discovery phase could make the people quite uncomfortable. There is no telling how they will respond.

At the same time, taking risks with new ideas includes finding a way to gain help from others and dealing with their opposition when they don't like what you have in mind. To overcome their resistance and win their support depends on your awareness of your ability to navigate the unpredictable.

—————— EXERCISE ——————

Rate your level of interpersonal risk tolerance described in the checklist below by putting an "x" in the appropriate box for each statement.

CHECKLIST: YOUR INTERPERSONAL RISK TOLERANCE

		Yes	No	Not often enough
1	I will ask for things from people I don't know.			
2	I take time to ask questions to learn about people I don't know or who make me feel uncomfortable.			
3	I change my communication style to fit the situation, even when it means a style that is very different from my usual style.			
4	I will talk with people who make me feel uncomfortable.			
5	I am not afraid to be wrong in a conversation.			
6	I admit when I am wrong to the people with whom I was wrong.			
7	I will talk with someone I don't know rather than email or text him or her.			
8	I will talk with someone I don't like or who makes me uncomfortable rather than email or text him or her.			
9	I will ask others for help in dealing with difficult persons or situations.			
10	I am willing to be patient and take the time to build a relationship with persons who make me feel uncomfortable.			

1. Based on your responses in the checklist, how would you describe your level of interpersonal risk tolerance? For example, you see you have a low risk tolerance for many different interpersonal scenarios.

_____

_____

_____

_____

2. Do you notice any themes arising from your answers in the checklist? For example, you might observe that you tend to avoid situations where you might be wrong or not in control.

_____

_____

_____

_____

———————————————— EXERCISE ————————————————

Make a list of the behaviors on the checklist where you need to work on interacting with others (that is, the behaviors in the Checklist: Your Interpersonal Risk Tolerance where you either marked yourself with a "No" or a "Not often enough").

1. _____

2. _____

3. _____

4. _____

Develop a plan for each behavior on the list where you marked a "No" or "Not often enough" to improve your interpersonal risk tolerance. Consider engaging the help of a trusted colleague, friend, or advisor for feedback and ideas. Use whatever form works for you (list, descriptive paragraphs, flow chart, etc.).

Example of an Interpersonal
Risk Tolerance Improvement Plan

Suppose you gave yourself a "No" on number 4 ("I will talk with people who make me feel uncomfortable"). To improve your ability to deal with people who make you uncomfortable, a plan might include the following actions.

Choose someone to interact with who makes you uncomfortable.

List why you believe that person makes you are uncomfortable. For example,

- He is condescending and super critical.
- He reminds you of someone with whom you had a bad experience.
- He is someone with whom you had a bad experience.
- You are an extrovert; he is an introvert; and you don't know how to deal effectively with introverts.
- You don't know anything about him.

List what you know and don't know about the person.

- What is his typical behavior?
- What communication style does he prefer?
- Who gets along with him and why? (bonus: and how?)
- What does he care most about professionally and personally?

Seek the answers to what you don't know from mutual colleagues, trusted mentors who know him, and other sources.

Develop a plan with what you need from that person and how you could best approach him. **Don't forget to analyze the hooks** his behavior might be triggering in you and how you will unhook them. (See Chapter 5 to learn how.)

Meet with the person for a normal business purpose. If the person is a friend, find a situation where it would be natural for you to meet (kids' soccer field, another friend's party, etc.). Pay attention to how the encounter goes.

Journal how you did, including what went well, what could have gone better, and your next steps with that person.

3. Interpersonal Risk Tolerance Plan Debrief: How did things go when you implemented your plan (or plans)? What did you learn? Did anything surprise you? If so, what? If you can, discuss your experiences with a trusted colleague, friend, or mentor.

_____

_____

_____

_____

_____

_____

_____

_____

_____

_____

_____

_____

_____

JOURNEY MILEPOST
The Risk of the Unknown

Navigating the world of new ideas lands you in the front of people and situations you do not know or expect. The discomfort of these encounters is a normal reaction to the risk of not knowing how things will go. Your job is to build awareness of how you respond to situations where you don't know the outcome ahead of time. Do you see them as a threat or an opportunity?

Learning how you respond to stress and accepting your reactions as part of the normal process of facing the new will free your energy to explore, discover, and make new ideas happen.

CHAPTER 5

Hooks
Watch Out for Self-Sabotaging Behaviors

THE KEY QUESTIONS

▶ 1. WHAT IS YOUR CURRENT HOOK CYCLE?

▶ 2. HOW WILL YOU BREAK OUT OF A NEGATIVE, SELF-SABOTAGING HOOK CYCLE TO ACHIEVE YOUR BIGGER BET?

▶ 3. HOW WILL YOU CREATE A NEW AND MORE SUCCESSFUL CYCLE?

WHAT ARE HOOKS AND HOW DO THEY WORK?

When confronted with uncomfortable, risky situations on the way to your bigger bet, defending yourself with behaviors that bring comfort is highly tempting. Leaning into that temptation is, well, tempting. Defenses represent a normal reaction to risk, even when risk leads to growth. Everyone has them. They protect you from pain, allowing you to function in a world that is not always fair or happy. Defenses give you the ability to work around difficult situations and do as well as you can when much is out of your control.

Defensive behaviors become "hooks" when they stand in the way of you accomplishing your bigger bets. They also can knock you off the road to your dream.

Avoiding defensive behaviors is hard, because while you are in the uncomfortable process of promoting a bigger bet, those whose support you want might respond with negativity.

- Tepid buy-in (said in a flat voice): "Oh . . . interesting . . ."

- Criticism (said in a condescending voice): "Well . . . the problem with **that** is _____ [fill in the blank]."

- Passive aggression (said in a surreal sweet voice): "Gee, I wish I had time to help, but I'm on deck to finish _____ [fill in the blank with someone else's project]."

Sound familiar? New ideas with unknown results can cause people to react defensively to cope with the scariness of change. Their walls of resistance will rise. The highest walls, however, might be yours.

If you are momentarily bored, playing with the layout of the presentation boards offers a nice diversion. If, however, you find yourself directing others to rearrange the layout, fonts, and other details to avoid dealing with the questionable strategy behind the presentation, then you are "hooked." You will lose your way toward pursuing your bigger bet.

Hooks appear in many forms and are familiar to anyone who has spent time in or outside of the work world. The ten most common hooks appear in the following table. For a more thorough description of each hook, consult Part 4 of the *Journey* book.

Hooks at a Glance

Hook Categories	Hooks	Description	Underlying Motivators
Operational Hooks		**"Do. Do. Do."** The task orientation that gets in the way of a broader strategic mindset.	Need for immediate feedback to counter anxiety of not knowing whether a bigger bet will be successful
	Micromanagement	Controlling the work of others with excessive attention to details.	Fear of loss of control
	Perfectionism	Setting a high standard of quality for work that cannot be achieved.	Fear of failure
	Conflict Avoidance	Not engaging in a conflict to avoid the stress of an unknown response from another. Avoidant behaviors include capitulation, disappearance, passive aggression, and bullying.	Fear of standing alone
	Codependence	Making one's own success and happiness dependent on enabling the success and happiness of someone else.	Fear of standing alone
Individual Contributor Hooks		**"Me. Me. Me"** Thinking in terms of one's own success rather than that of the enterprise.	Concern over one's value to the organization
	Taking the Credit	Taking credit for the accomplishments of others.	Anxiety over importance to the organization
	Personalizing	Not distinguishing one's personal value from the value to the organization.	Lack of self-esteem
	Failure to Delegate	Being unable or reluctant to involve others in the delivery of work.	Lack of trust
Invisibility Hooks		**"Who. Who. Who."** The disbelief that everyone is watching you.	Resistance to being the barometer of the organization on the basis of which everyone decides what to believe and how to behave
	Disengagement	Withdrawing physically or mentally from involvement in an activity, situation, or personal interaction.	Loss of privacy
	Poor Boundaries	Sharing information with others that is inappropriate for them to receive.	Loss of the validating support of a peer group
	Inauthenticity	Acting in a manner that is inconsistent with one's personality to mask the discomfort of not knowing something.	Fear of being fallible

Hook Cycles: A Primer

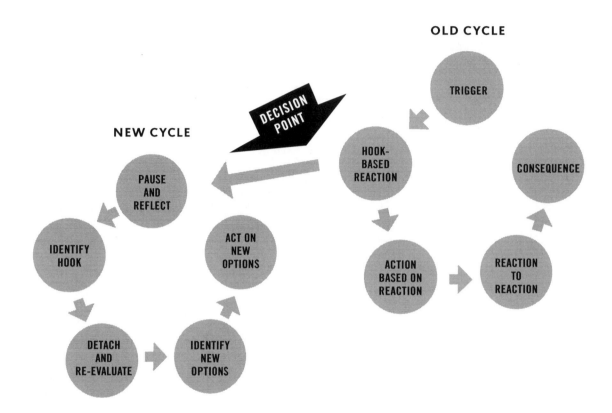

You are in the midst of testing a new idea when somebody says or does something that causes you to feel uncomfortable. That upsetting event is a trigger. As shown in the graphic above, a trigger sets in motion a hook cycle. Your challenge is to recognize the trigger before it morphs into a hooked chain reaction of negative consequences. If you catch it before the hook sets in, then you can decide to build a more informed and strategic response to the triggering event and focus on pursuing your bigger bet.

To illustrate how old hook cycles and new hook cycles work, consider the following example.

MARGOT'S STORY

Margot, a talented senior project manager, wanted a promotion to director level. In pursuit of that goal, her bigger bet was to provide exemplary service to her clients, trying out innovative ideas wherever possible. While it made her nervous when she took on the risk of new ideas, it looked like they were working.

That is, until the day she heard that Michael, a project manager who reported to her, told Ian, her supervisor, that her biggest client was unhappy with her team.

Hearing of the client's dissatisfaction triggered a wounded feeling in Margot. She took the matter personally, feeling blamed and worthless for the failure to please the client. She also was angry with Michael, who she believed should have told her, not Ian, about the client's unhappiness. She also assumed he purposely played the male colleague card by going around her directly to Ian.

Instead of talking to Michael, Margot complained to Ian about Michael not telling her about the client's unhappiness. She finished by accusing Michael of being a male chauvinist pig. Ian shuddered inside when he heard her say that. Rather than sympathizing, he concluded she was not effectively leading her group. Prior to this incident, Ian had considered promoting her, but now he decided to defer the promotion until she proved to him she could build a more cohesive team.

THE OLD HOOK CYCLE

An old hook cycle starts with an event that triggers discomfort in you and causes you to become "hooked" to defend yourself.

———————— EXERCISE ————————

Describe your reaction to Margot's story and how you believe she did or did not handle things well.

_____

_____

_____

Does any part of the story make you cringe? If so, what and why?

_____

_____

_____

MARGOT'S OLD HOOK CYCLE

Here are the steps of an old hook cycle. For each step, write how you think they appear in Margot's story.

Trigger: A trigger is an event that causes discomfort. The event can be such things as a verbal attack from a colleague, a client demand for a project with an unforgiving deadline, or a competing company stealing a top performer. Whatever the event, it is often unexpected and causes significant stress.

Margot's trigger: _____

Hook-based reaction: A hook-based reaction occurs when you seek comfort to escape the stress of the triggering event by adopting one or more hooks.

Margot's hook-based reaction: _____

_____

Action based on reaction: When a person becomes hooked by one or more of their hooks, they will act from an emotional rather than a fact-based place.

Margot's action based on her reaction: _____

_____

Reaction to reaction: When you react with a hook, others will draw their own conclusions about the event.

Ian's reaction to Margot's reaction: _____

_____

Consequence: Focusing on defending yourself from the stress of unwelcome behavior will prevent you from taking in the larger picture that could lead to bigger bets.

The consequence to Margot's career: _____

_____

ANSWER KEY FOR MARGOT'S NEGATIVE HOOK CYCLE

Here are some starting points for answers on how Margot's negative hook cycle showed up in the story and additional information to promote further understanding.

Trigger: Margot's trigger was hearing criticism about her work.

Hook-based reaction: When Margot heard that the client was unhappy with her team, rather than asking Michael what the client said, she defended herself with a personalizing hook.

Margot grew up in a shaming and blaming family. When things went wrong, she automatically assumed it was due to her personal shortcomings. Her parents seemed content to go along with her assumption. In her adult life, that old habit of personalizing prevented her from seeing the bigger picture.

Because she confused the client dissatisfaction with her value as a person, she missed learning from Michael and the client what had led to the client's unhappiness.

Action based on reaction: Instead of taking the time to understand what Michael actually did, Margot's reactive, hooked behavior caused her to attack him by complaining to Ian. Had she been less emotionally reactive, she would have realized that going directly to her supervisor showed poor judgment. Instead, she focused on her hurt feelings of being blamed. That sent her looking for an opportunity to hurt someone else (Michael) rather than digging deeper into what she did not know about Michael or the client.

Reaction to reaction: Ian expected Margot to build team unity. That requires strong intra-team communication. He viewed her failure to ask Michael what he had learned from the client as poor leadership.

Consequence: Margot's preoccupation with the blow to her self-esteem stopped her from talking with Michael or the client. A consequence of her failure to do so resulted in her promotion being deferred and she having to prove herself again with Ian.

The New Hook Cycle

When Margot heard of the client's criticism, she had a choice. She could either go into a reactive, hooked place and suffer the negative consequences that it caused, or she could decide to work through her discomfort to investigate what she did not know about the situation and solve the problem with constructive ideas and behavior.

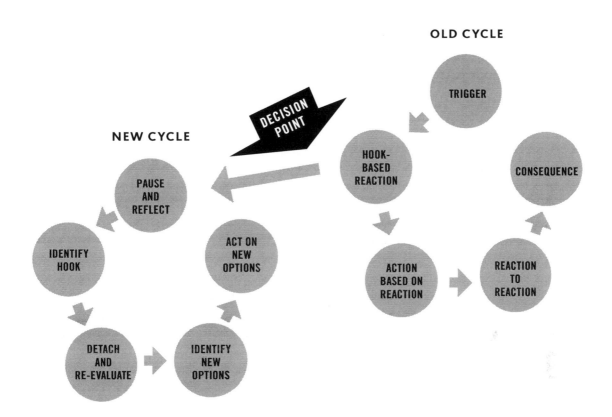

─────────────── EXERCISE ───────────────

How might Margot have responded differently and more successfully to her situation?

_____

_____

_____

_____

MARGOT'S NEW HOOK CYCLE

The critical first step toward breaking an old, reactive hook cycle is to recognize when an event triggers a defensive response in you. Below are the steps for shifting from a triggering event leading to a negative hook cycle to a new and more successful cycle that keeps you on the road to your bigger bet.

As shown in the diagram, the steps of creating a new cycle are as follows.

Trigger: The new cycle begins with the awareness that a hook has grabbed hold. You might not know at the time what hook it is. However, to adopt a new, more successful behavior, it is enough to recognize that you have been triggered by something and are responding defensively with a hook. Margot recognized that criticism triggered anger and defensiveness in her.

Pause and Reflect: Taking a deep breath, becoming quiet, or doing anything else that breaks the hook-based reaction will point you in the direction of a new cycle. It slows the speeding train of defensive behavior. It also allows for detachment from the stress of the situation and opens your field of vision to see better what is "going on in the room."

When Margot became anxious, she needed to process her feelings out loud to reduce her reactivity. She called her executive coach to discuss the Michael incident. Talking it through helped to cool her down. In a less emotionally charged state, she could come up with good questions to ask Michael about what he heard from the client, and why he spoke to Ian rather than to her.

Identify Hook: Identifying what hook is catching you will help you understand its characteristics and map a new strategy. Upon reflection, Margot realized that she had been grabbed by a personalizing hook. She had taken the client feedback as a judgment about her value as human being rather than the value of her company's client service.

JOURNEY SNIPPET

Claudia Milgram, the chief financial officer of Arrow, Inc., did not like anyone telling her what to do. When Barry Sanford, the Arrow chief executive officer, asked her to produce a different set of reports for the Porter proposal, she interpreted his request as an attack on her carefully processed, mistake-proof, financial reporting.

Serendipitously, as she was fuming about his request, a colleague of hers suddenly appeared, also complaining about Barry. Claudia listened and recognized how that coworker's annoyance was caused by personal rather than professional reasons. It inspired Claudia to put a mirror up to her own reaction to Barry. She noticed her sharp, angry response was way out of proportion with Barry's request and that she had been triggered.

She then was able to identify a perfectionist hook and how it could only lead to a negative outcome for her. With the benefit of that insight, she thought about why she went that route and how it was getting in the way of her career advancement. That started her on the road to a new strategy.

Detach and Re-evaluate: When a hook grabs hold, it is easy to beat yourself up for less-than-ideal behavior. However, remember that defenses alleviate the pain caused by a stressful event. There is nothing wrong with pain relief. When a defensive behavior prevents you from pursuing your bigger bet, it becomes a hook. To unhook the hook, give yourself compassion. After all, we are all flawed humans just trying to make our way. Then you can get to work on changing your behavior.

When Margot recognized that she had personalized the client's reaction, she was able to start detaching from its emotional charge. Draining some of the emotionalism out of the situation allowed her to step back and survey the bigger picture. She realized she didn't know what Michael had intended or what specifically had made the client unhappy.

Identify New Options: Once you have forgiven yourself, your field of vision widens, and you can identify new and more effective strategies to resolve a situation. Margot embarked on a mission to learn what she had not known before. Her first conversation was with Michael.

She realized she didn't know Michael. When she finally spent time with him, she discovered that prior to his employment at her company, he had been self-employed. The idea of going through a chain of command to communicate information was foreign to him. He had merely bumped into Ian in the coffee room just after he learned of the client's complaint. For him, passing on the client feedback was a natural act of relaying what he had just heard that might be helpful. That his comment to Ian would be viewed as undercutting the value of Margot had never entered his mind.

Act on New Options: A new approach might involve different behavior for you. With the benefit of more understanding as to Michael's motivation, Margot worked on developing a productive relationship with him. Together, they approached the client to learn about the concerns. Then they developed a plan to remedy them. Finally, they put the plan in place and met the client's needs. They also were able to build a strong working relationship with each other. A few months later, Ian promoted Margot to director.

Journey Snippet

Marco Perez, Arrow's vice president of operations, took great pride in his project management systems and his ability to please everyone. People found him agreeable, efficient, and careful. He liked that. He also liked to avoid conflict, fearing that honest conversation could cost him his job. That actually occurred in his previous company. While he still believed in what he did at the time, he decided at Arrow he would keep his head down and not risk speaking up in case there was something he did not know that could hurt him.

When the Porter deal came along, he knew someone at Porter who might know the motive behind the question about Arrow being fired. At first, Marco decided to not pursue his source, choosing instead to remain quiet and safe. He had known that person in his previous company. It was he who passed on Marco's discovery of false financial information to a senior manager who turned out to be chummy with the manager who had falsified the information. He wanted to avoid dealing with that guy no matter what, even though he knew his former coworker didn't realize his action would lead to a political response that ended Marco's job.

Marco's avoidant strategy changed when Barry Sanford, Arrow's CEO, confronted him for not talking to his contact. Marco saw that in this situation, his conflict avoidance could hurt Arrow's pursuit of its bigger bet, the Porter deal, and, closer to home, his career. In other words, his conflict avoidant hook could jeopardize his Arrow job.

With that possible consequence, Marco realized his former coworker probably owed him something. He pushed through his nervousness about how he might respond and asked him about the Porter deal. What Marco learned helped answer Arrow's question about Porter's motive. He also found an appetite for taking more chances.

LESSONS FROM THE FRONT
The Power of Silent Observation

Calvin hated when people challenged his ideas at meetings. Normally, he reacted to opposition by vigorously defending himself. Rather than winning buy-in for his ideas, his defensiveness merely ignited more arguments. After a number of such meetings, his colleagues complained to senior leadership that they did not like working with him due to his negativity.

The Intervention: Charlotte, Calvin's supervisor, delivered the feedback to him. His colleagues' feedback surprised him. At the same time, he knew that without their support, his proposals for new initiatives would founder. He set to work with Charlotte on an improvement plan. After a long conversation, he reluctantly admitted that criticism triggered anxiety in him. He personalized the pushback of others, experiencing it as a judgment of him, rather than of his ideas. With the benefit of that insight, he decided to break his personalizing hook cycle and try a new strategy.

The Experiment: At the next meeting with his colleagues, he presented a new initiative and waited for reactions. A couple of people took potshots at it. That bothered him, but he caught himself by gritting his teeth and merely nodding his head to say he had heard. It wasn't easy, but it stopped the speeding train of negative reactions.

Then he tried a different strategy. He decided to remain quiet while he studied each person in the room. The silence felt weird. Business people avoid it at all costs because they fear losing control. In reality, silence can lend a powerful pause that moves the focus of the room to the person who became quiet. When Calvin wordlessly observed each member of the meeting, he discovered that rather than the others opposing him, several looked confused, distracted by their smartphones, or nervous about something.

The Revelation: Calvin realized his colleagues might not have disagreed but rather wanted to understand his idea better or had other things on their minds. From previous meetings, he also suspected some of them needed more time to process it. This happens often with introverted colleagues who work better when given private time to process ideas before deciding what they think about them.

The Result: With the many circumstances in play, Calvin shifted his style from defending his position to asking his audience questions about their level of understanding, interest, and whether they needed more time to consider the idea. They responded positively. Calvin left the meeting with a plan that the others supported.

▶ 1. WHAT IS YOUR CURRENT HOOK CYCLE?

Overcoming hooks and their negative impacts on bigger bets starts with recognizing when they appear. Hooks surface in many forms and vary by the individual and situation.

──────── EXERCISE ────────

Describe a time when you were trying out a new idea or behavior and someone or something upset you in a way that caused you to react defensively, and your defensive reaction set in motion a chain of events that did not end well.

_____

_____

_____

_____

_____

_____

▶ 2. HOW WILL YOU BREAK OUT OF A NEGATIVE, SELF-SABOTAGING HOOK CYCLE TO ACHIEVE YOUR BIGGER BET?

──────── EXERCISE ────────

Using an example of one of your current hook cycles, answer the following questions.

TRIGGER

What was said or done that set you off and triggered a defensive reaction?

_____

_____

_____

_____

STUDY AID
Triggers

Reflecting on the incident you chose as an example of a time when you reacted defensively, think about how it began. What was said or done that set you off? Below are some examples of triggering events.

- A colleague attacked me in front of my team.

- My manager said my presentation was awful.

- I was excluded from participating in a discussion group attended by my peers.

- A client told me she wasn't happy with our work.

- My best friend criticized how I organized our annual neighborhood fundraiser.

- The local newspaper wrote an article about our new school initiative and entirely missed the point of what we are trying to do, despite me having spent an hour talking with the reporter.

How did you react when triggered? Circle the reactions below that apply to you.

I am afraid.   I hate this.

It's stupid.   Yawn, it's boring.

I'm not interested.

I want to get through this as fast as possible.

I'm annoyed.   **I'm scared.**

I want to run. I feel stirred up.

I feel anxious.   *I don't like this person.*

I am afraid something will happen, or won't happen and that would be bad.

Add your own. _____

_____

_____

_____

_____

HOOK-BASED REACTION

You've been triggered. Now what? Hooks can be experienced in many different ways and vary by individuals. People notice a wide variety of reactions, including anxiety, annoyance, or even calm as they distance themselves from the stress caused by the situation.

Can you recognize when you react defensively? Below are some examples of how people feel when they shift into a defensive or "hooked" reaction. Circle any that apply to you. If none apply or you have other reactions, write them in the space provided below the box.

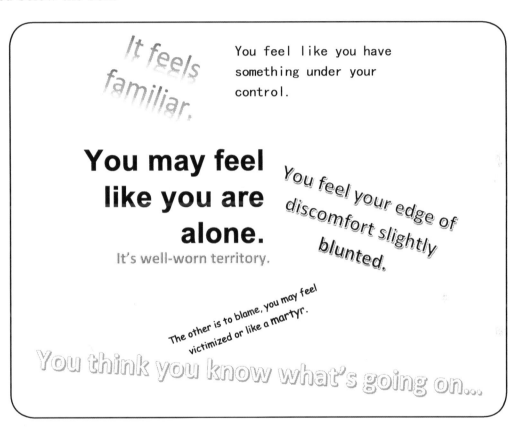

It feels familiar.

You feel like you have something under your control.

You may feel like you are alone.

It's well-worn territory.

You feel your edge of discomfort slightly blunted.

The other is to blame, you may feel victimized or like a martyr.

You think you know what's going on...

_____

_____

_____

_____

ACTION BASED ON REACTION

What action did you take after you became hooked?

_____

_____

_____

_____

REACTION TO REACTION

How did the other person or persons react to your action?

_____

_____

_____

_____

CONSEQUENCE

What was the final result?

_____

_____

_____

_____

▶ 3. HOW WILL YOU CREATE A NEW AND MORE SUCCESSFUL CYCLE?

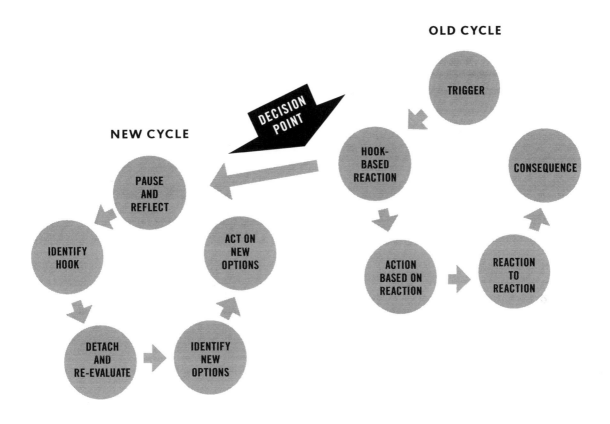

─── EXERCISE ───

Imagine that you could have a do-over. Given the chance, how would you have acted differently in the situation you just described?

_____

_____

_____

_____

_____

Trigger: When the triggering event occurred, what physical or emotional reaction might you recognize in time to catch yourself and choose a different approach to the situation?

_____

_____

_____

_____

Pause and Reflect: What might you do to slow your reactivity?

_____

_____

_____

_____

Identify Hook: What hook or hooks were grabbing you? How did they show up in your behavior? How were you feeling at the time?

_____

_____

_____

_____

Detach and Re-evaluate: As your emotional reactivity starts to decrease, what do you notice about your situation that you might not have seen before?

_____

_____

_____

_____

Identify New Options: With the benefit of a less emotionally charged state of mind, what might you do differently to resolve your situation?

_____

_____

_____

_____

JOURNEY SNIPPET

In a vulnerable moment, Janelle Wilbert, the tightly wound Arrow general counsel, admitted to Claudia that Barry's requests made her crazy, because she could not possibly produce high-quality work with so many demands on her time. Barry's most recent request involved the Porter proposal, which had the entire leadership team in a tailspin. Nevertheless, Janelle viewed it as another assault on her carefully monitored time and work product.

Seeing Janelle's agitation, Claudia suggested that Barry's actions might have triggered memories of how in her family, Janelle had been responsible for bringing order to the chaotic lives of the other family members. Janelle reacted to her need to establish order in her family's home with a perfectionism that followed her into her work life.

When Claudia reminded her that she shouldered the family organizing role because she cared about them, Janelle realized she could apply the same motivation to her work life. She cared about Barry and the rest of the team. That admission allowed her to relax her need for perfectionism to support, rather than thwart, Barry to win the Porter deal.

Act on New Options: If possible, put your do-over plan in motion. Pay attention to what you learned when you chose a different approach to the original problem. If the opportunity has passed, watch for another and apply your changed approach to it.

FREE WRITE

Write what happened, how others reacted, and how you felt about the result.

_____

_____

_____

_____

JOURNEY SNIPPET

When Claudia applied her new options to the broader goals of Arrow winning valuable new client work and advancing her career, she delivered to Barry the reports he wanted for the Porter proposal. She then made a point of getting more involved with the company outside of the finance team. She shadowed members of the operations and engineering teams to learn more about the business. In doing that, Claudia built a stronger connection with the leadership team.

She further strengthened her team connection by showing her human side. One day, she brought her daughter to visit the office. She had not done that before, fearing that others would not take her seriously as a professional if she were seen as a doting parent. Allowing her coworkers to meet her daughter and to let them know how deeply she loved her was a major step for her.

Lessons from the Front
How Do You Break Out of Your Hooks in the Long Term?

On-Stage Work

Hooks tend to appear when you are least prepared. A new customer calls out of the blue to tell you how badly they think your project with them is going. You learn from a peer that a project you championed was exposed to ridicule in the press. A team member attacks you at a meeting in front of your direct reports. No doubt, these are difficult moments. They are also opportunities.

Learning to recognize your hooks in the moment and finding a more successful strategy is the "on-stage" work, which involves learning to become aware that a hook has caught you at the moment it occurs. Then you use your awareness to stop a reactive "hooked" mode, regroup in the moment, and build a new cycle with a better strategy for you and the organization.

Off-Stage Work

To sustain learning to recognize hooks and strategies to overcome them, it is important to do the "off-stage" work, which centers on understanding what set off your hook in the first place. We all have personal history that encodes into our current behavior, often below our level of consciousness. Its influence can be profound both on our feelings and actions. Discovering the source of our hooks empowers us to make better choices.

There are many ways to unearth the roots of our feelings. Paying attention to our feelings is an obvious beginning. From there, we can learn more by using a wide range of tools, including journaling, insight from colleagues and friends, reading relevant literature, coaching, and therapy.

Journey Milepost

Uncovering and decoding your behavior to know what makes you uncomfortable and defensive takes hard work. Yet without that work, you limit your ability to stretch into the unknown and take the risks needed to bring about change.

Knowing more about yourself does not mean you can eliminate the past. **You cannot change your life stories, but you can change how you behave as a result of them.**

CHAPTER 6

Drivers
Find Drivers to Give You Fuel

THE KEY QUESTIONS

▶ 1. WHAT PURPOSE WILL GIVE YOU FUEL TO NAVIGATE THE DISCOMFORT OF THE UNKNOWN TOWARD YOUR BIGGER BET?

▶ 2. WHAT CORE PURPOSE WILL GIVE YOU THE MOST POWER THROUGH THE DISCOMFORT OF THE UNKNOWN?

WHAT ARE DRIVERS?

Finding opportunities in the new does not mean just grinding through the pain of discovery and adversity. You need a good reason to go through the discomfort of driving change.

Drivers give you a purpose for undertaking the journey to bigger bets. A driver can be situational, tied to the needs of a particular set of circumstances, such as taking on Toastmaster training to prove to one's partners that you can stand in front of an audience and win business.

Even more powerful are core drivers. Core drivers pull from your fundamental beliefs, values, and life story.

Sir Richard Branson tells the story of how his dyslexia made him appear less intelligent than he really was. With the encouragement of his grandmother, who insisted he had only one life to live and he better live it well, he put his energy into connecting people and ideas.

During his adolescence, he managed to combine the newspapers of several schools in one magazine called *Student*. He then convinced merchants that their advertising in the magazine would reach a large audience. That strategy worked particularly well with record sellers. One thing led to another and Branson formed the now famous and successful Virgin Group, starting with selling discounted records to students. Overcoming his dyslexia became a strong core driver for him that led to huge professional success.

▶ **1. WHAT PURPOSE WILL GIVE YOU FUEL TO NAVIGATE THE DISCOMFORT OF THE UNKNOWN TOWARD YOUR BIGGER BET?**

Situational drivers provide motivation for dealing with tough situations because the cost of not facing them is worse. Deciding that there is no way you want a certain competitor to beat you can furnish you with motivation to endure the anxiety of assembling a winning proposal. That anxiety might include working with your ruthless and unpredictable business strategy team, who intimidate you but whose analytical talent you need to beat the competition.

Think of a time when to win, you had to do something new and scary to you. What motivated you to push through the scariness to keep moving forward?

_____

_____

_____

_____

JOURNEY SNIPPET

Nigel Johnson, the Arrow, Inc., vice president of sales, prided himself in being a top sales executive. He lived on the road, where he won the business and loyalty of many customers. Losing the highly visible Porter deal could hurt his reputation in the marketplace. Even closer to home, however, was the handsome sales commission that he had promised to his wife as a thank you for all the time he spent away from her taking care of his parents. Focusing on winning the Porter commission would sustain his reputation and, better yet, provide a gift to his deserving wife.

Core drivers make people who they are. They often come from early life, resulting from family dynamics or life experiences outside of the family in school or the work world.

A core driver can originate with an overbearing parent who does not want you to achieve more than they did in the world, a death of the nurturing family member who compelled you to accomplish something in honor of them, or a cherished friend who inspires you by their own life and expresses a strong belief in your ability to do the same.

▶ 2. WHAT CORE PURPOSE WILL GIVE YOU THE MOST POWER THROUGH THE DISCOMFORT OF THE UNKNOWN?

Core drivers are more challenging to identify than situational drivers, as they are intensely personal, often derived from early life experiences. Arriving at what provides you with the most meaningful motivation to weave through the halls of new initiatives will take time, not to mention trial and error. Core drivers also evolve, as you grow more self-aware.

Here are some questions to assist you in your thought process.

———————————— EXERCISE ————————————

1. What gives you meaning?

Describe an event in your life where you plunged forward, despite your fears, because what you wanted to achieve outweighed the fear of getting there. Consider choosing an event when you triumphed over adversity, which might make it easier to access strong feelings and beliefs.

If you'd rather not go the adversity route, think about an event where you accomplished something you considered a triumph. The accomplishment must be something you caused to happen, did well, enjoyed doing, and made you proud. It can include such talents as having a strong ability to analyze, mediate emotionally charged situations, or figure out clever and unusual technical solutions. It is something on which you have relied throughout your life because it has brought you success in many situations.*

_____

_____

_____

_____

*Bernard Haldane and Peter Ferdinand Drucker, *Career Satisfaction and Success: A Guide to Job and Personal Freedom*, Jist Works; Revised (1995).

_____

_____

_____

_____

_____

_____

_____

_____

2. What are your values?

Values are those beliefs you hold most dear about what matters in the world and how you live in it. They include such things as honesty, service, hard work, loving one's neighbors, pushing the envelope, and working for a greater good to make a difference.

What values are most important to you and why?

_____

_____

_____

_____

_____

_____

_____

_____

_____

_____

_____

JOURNEY SNIPPET

Barry Sanford, the CEO of Arrow, Inc., had spent the whole day trying to persuade each member of his leadership team to find the information needed to satisfy Porter's request. He had gotten nowhere. Instead, he smacked into solid walls of resistance. That depressed him. Not only was he getting no closer to fulfilling the Porter request, he realized how fractured his relationships were with his team. How did that happen? He stared out the window mulling over his interactions that day with each of his executives.

He had always placed a high value on connection with others. The late-afternoon sun shining into his office reminded him of growing up with a disengaged father. Barry used to visit his father in his office and saw that he never looked happy. Barry vowed that in his own life, he would not repeat his father's misery. Instead, he would make connecting with others a priority.

During his late-afternoon reflection, Barry admitted to himself that he had lost track of his personal value about connecting. Instead he had been ignoring his team. By doing so, he put a damper on the free flow of information from his team members that was vital to winning clients like Porter. It was time to change his behavior and live in accordance with his deeply held values about connecting, starting with his leadership team.

---

3. What are your dreams for the future?

Paint a picture of your utopia, in other words, if everything were perfect with no constraints, how would it look? If it aids your creativity, see 4. Optional opportunity.

_____

_____

_____

_____

4. Optional opportunity: Here's a chance to access your inner Picasso. Draw a picture of your utopia. No one has to see what you create, so go ahead. Lift your colored pens and allow the images to unfold.

Lessons from the Front
"Oh, Yes, I Will"

Over the years, I have heard a surprising number of stories from women whose mothers told them they would fail. Without going into the possible psychology of that attitude, those doubting mothers did provide their daughters with strong drivers.

In the *Journey* book, I included the story of the five-year-old daughter of a commercial office building cleaner. One night when she accompanied her mom on her cleaning rounds, she jumped into the empty chair of the chief executive officer of the company whose office the girl's mother was cleaning. When the little girl bounded into the big swivel chair, her mother yelled in horror, "You get out of that chair! You will NEVER sit in that chair!" The little girl was shocked and confused by what her mother said.

The impact of those words stayed with her and formed a powerful core driver. At the time she said nothing to her mother, but promptly jumped out of the chair. Inside, however, she said to herself, "Oh, yes, I will." Thirty years later she was the owner and CEO of a medium-sized, property management company.

5. What are your non-negotiables? What are those things that you must have to feel successful? What are things you will not do? For example, is it important that you are viewed as an expert with a pristine reputation for originality and thorough work? Do you want to make sure that you either will or will not be associated with a certain polit

_____

_____

_____

_____

———— EXERCISE ————

What is your core driver?

Read back through this chapter to review what you wrote (and drew, if you expressed your inner Picasso). When you combine what you said (and drew), what themes do you see that could point to your core driver? It does not have to beautifully worded. It just has to hold meaning for you.

_____

_____

_____

_____

LESSONS FROM THE FRONT
Changing Drivers with Changing Circumstances

Drivers can change when on the way to a bigger bet, the conditions supporting the bigger bet change. A dramatic example of this appears in the story *Endurance* (Alfred Lansing, Carroll & Graff Publishers, Inc., 1959).

In 1914, British explorer William Shackleton planned to cross Antarctica on foot, because it was the last uncharted continent in the world. If he achieved that goal, he would gain great notoriety in the lofty world of British explorers. That formed a strong personal driver for him.

Unfortunately, when his ship reached Antarctica, winter arrived early. The ship became locked in ice, cutting off his crew and him from the rest of the world. Viewing this dire situation, Shackleton's motivating driver changed from cementing his reputation as a premier world explorer to making sure every one of his twenty-seven crew members made it home alive.

It informed his many leadership decisions to overcome a constant series of life-threatening challenges. Two years later, Shackleton and all twenty-seven crewmembers were rescued.

LESSONS FROM THE FRONT
When Entering the Unknown Takes You Elsewhere

"Charging into the unknown, trusting your mind, gut, and heart allows you to embark on a journey to bring out your authentic self."

This comment came from a former bank executive, who left the security of her long-term banking career to follow her dream of becoming an interior designer. While she had known for a long time that she loved beautiful design, she questioned how she could build a career based on it. Aside from her financial obligations to her family, she also worried whether she could make it work. She excelled in operations, something that served her well in the banking world. She had no idea whether there was a place for her in the interior design world, having never tried it.

Nevertheless, she continued to be intrigued by the design industry. She spent time researching it, exploring its products, and meeting people who worked in it. While she continued to be successful as a bank executive, the idea of switching to interior design only intensified. Finally, when she had taken care of her family and other commitments, she followed her heart and went to interior design school. Today she is a happy interior design professional.

ASSEMBLING THE NEW CYCLE WITH A DRIVER

With the benefit of the right driver to propel you through discomfort, you can put into action your new ideas and behaviors. You might feel uneasy and awkward when you first behave in a different way. Others might also find it disconcerting and try to push you back into your old behavior to escape their discomfort. Your job is to pull from your driver and maintain a forward movement. The more you practice new behaviors, the easier they will become for you.

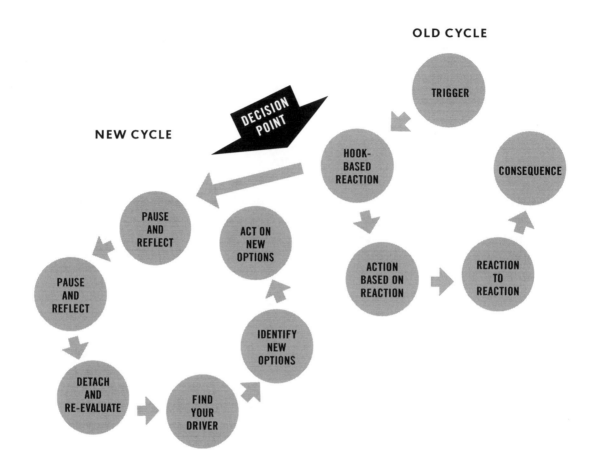

JOURNEY MILEPOST
Driver Fuel

The deeper the core driver, the more fuel it will give you to weave through the labyrinth of uncertainty. The more you draw on what you learn about your life histories, values, and dreams, the more energy you will have to achieve your bigger bets.

CHAPTER 7

Assembling the Roadmap

In the previous six chapters, you explored your relationship with the unknown and with the discomfort the unknown can cause. Then you worked on the Core Four principles as navigation tools to travel into the unknown as you champion new ideas.

The Journey of Not Knowing Roadmap

On the next page is a place for you to summarize your key learnings. Keep them simple, to be most memorable *and* actionable!

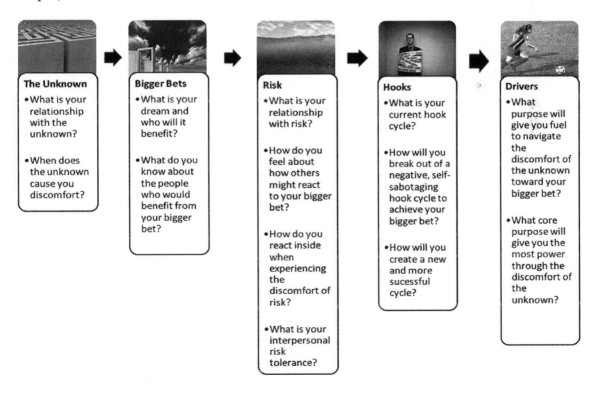

The Unknown
- What is your relationship with the unknown?
- When does the unknown cause you discomfort?

Bigger Bets
- What is your dream and who will it benefit?
- What do you know about the people who would benefit from your bigger bet?

Risk
- What is your relationship with risk?
- How do you feel about how others might react to your bigger bet?
- How do you react inside when experiencing the discomfort of risk?
- What is your interpersonal risk tolerance?

Hooks
- What is your current hook cycle?
- How will you break out of a negative, self-sabotaging hook cycle to achieve your bigger bet?
- How will you create a new and more sucessful cycle?

Drivers
- What purpose will give you fuel to navigate the discomfort of the unknown toward your bigger bet?
- What core purpose will give you the most power through the discomfort of the unknown?

Your Roadmap

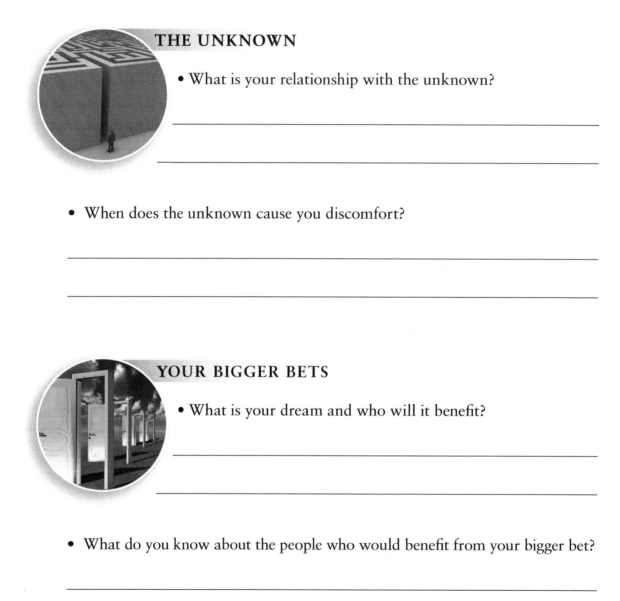

THE UNKNOWN

- What is your relationship with the unknown?

_____

_____

- When does the unknown cause you discomfort?

_____

_____

YOUR BIGGER BETS

- What is your dream and who will it benefit?

_____

_____

- What do you know about the people who would benefit from your bigger bet?

_____

_____

THE RISK OF THE UNKNOWN

- What is your relationship with risk?

_____

_____

- How do you feel about how others might react to your bigger bet?

_____

_____

- How do you react inside when experiencing the discomfort of risk?

_____

_____

- What is your interpersonal risk tolerance?

_____

_____

HOOKS

- What is your current hook cycle?

_____

_____

- How will you break out of your negative, self-sabotaging hook cycle to achieve your bigger bet?

_____

_____

- How will you create a new and more successful cycle?

_____

_____

DRIVERS

- What purpose will give you fuel to navigate the discomfort of the unknown toward your bigger bet?

_____

_____

- What core purpose will give you the most power through the discomfort of the unknown?

_____

_____

Final Reflections

Read through your summary in this chapter. Are there any final impressions, ideas, or insights you would like to add?

_____

_____

_____

_____

_____

_____

The Journey Forward

Congratulations on having given yourself the gift of time and attention by recording your reflections in this journal. That is no small feat in this time-pressured world with demands from so many directions. As you go forward, use your work in this journal to support and guide you on your journey to make life better.

Charting your course through the adventure of achieving your dreams will give you energy, direction, and purpose. There is nothing like making a difference, for others and yourself.

Welcome to the future!

Acknowledgments

While it appears that an acknowledgments page is not routine for workbooks, if I have learned nothing else from stepping into the world of book writing three years ago, I know that nothing happens without a vital community of subject matter experts, trusted colleagues, family, and friends. *The Journal of Not Knowing* has been no exception. In my effort to produce a guide for professional and personal development that engages its readers, inspires their growth, and delights the eye, I have been blessed with a talented and supportive community. I would like to thank all of them for their contributions, without which there would be no journal.

In our day of social media where the reach can be wide, I will focus my specific thanks here on those who were directly involved in the production of the book. For those who are not listed, my appreciation is no less sincere.

Without question, I must start with my husband and daughter, both of whom put up with my obsessive thinking, wordsmithing, and fretting over conceptual clarity. Mercifully, my family travels with a broad perspective and a sturdy sense of humor.

Indispensable to the conceptualization, wording, and design of this book is the team who worked with me on *The Journey of Not Knowing*. Gail Kearns of To Press & Beyond, my editor and book Sherpa, leant her sharp eye to advance content, editorial, and strategic direction as we strived to create a book that educates, entertains, and elevates its readers. Joni Wilson made sure the words met the highest standards of English writing and that the structure and form of the manuscript worked.

Alan Dino Hebel and Ian Koviak of *the*BookDesigners, who produced the award-winning cover for the *Journey* book, generated compelling and beautiful designs for the cover of this book and its interior.

Added to the team is Kathy Moran of Web Development Artistry, the web designer and technology expert for the website, newsletters, and the social media work for the book.

Equally important to creating a training and self-help workbook that promotes human development is the advice of training and development industry experts.

Deep thanks go to the peer reviewers who each brought many years of experience from their careers in human resources, training, and coaching. They took time out of their busy lives to read and provide feedback on the content and style of the book based on their extensive knowledge of personal and professional development. Those persons are (in alphabetical order) Brenda Bluemke, Maria Escobar-Bordyn, Diane Gilmore, Linda Jack, Jane Mounsey, Mary Jane Pioli, Pam Rechel, Stephanie Reynolds, and Jim Strain. A special shout out goes to Stephanie Reynolds for being my long-time business partner in The Journey of Not Knowing program, to Brenda Bluemke and Maria Escobar-Bordyn who in addition to giving advice, facilitate Journey programs and to Katie Urbain for her tireless work on the Journey website, graphics, and newsletter.

Last, but not at all least, is my former teaching partner, Karen Ellzey, who encouraged me to create this workbook and call it *The Journal of Not Knowing*.

Thank You

Thank you for reading my book. If you enjoyed it,
please take a moment to leave a review.

You might be interested in the companion book, *The Journey of Not Knowing:
How 21st-Century Leaders Can Chart a Course Where There Is None.*
See www.juliebenezet.com/book for links to purchasing options
in paperback, e-book, and audiobook formats.

About the Author

Julie Benezet has devoted her professional life to exploring the new, building businesses and helping others do the same. She currently works as a leadership consultant, teacher, and owner of The Journey of Not Knowing®, a leadership program she founded. She speaks and writes on leading and living in the twenty-first century and decoding human behavior in the face of change. Her book, *The Journey of Not Knowing: How 21st-Century Leaders Can Chart a Course Where There Is None*, received a 2017 Benjamin Franklin Gold Medal and the 2016 Foreword INDIES Book of the Year Silver Medal for Business & Economics.

Julie spent four years as a member of the Amazon.com leadership team that brought the company from the early steep ramp up phase to its emergence as a thriving enterprise. Before joining Amazon.com, Julie built businesses and raised capital for a broad range of industries from Fortune 100 companies to start-ups. She practiced law in New York and Seattle.

For ten years, Julie led the "Challenges of Leadership" program for executives at the Harvard Graduate School of Design. She has appeared in numerous publications including *The Wall Street Journal, The New York Times, Tech Republic.com, Training Industry,* and *The Zweig Letter.* She holds an LLB (law) and M.Sc. (psychology) from McGill University and a B.A. from Cornell University.

When she is not working, she loves to read mysteries, explore new wineries, and wander through compelling physical environments.

For more information, visit
www.juliebenezet.com

You can subscribe to her blog, "The View from the Treehouse," at
www.juliebenezet.com/blog

89375834R00078

Made in the USA
San Bernardino, CA
24 September 2018